MORE FROST AND SNOW

SOURCES IN LOCAL HISTORY No2

The Sources in Local History series is
sponsored by the *European Ethnological
Research Centre* c/o the National Museums
of Scotland, Queen Street, Edinburgh
EH2 1JD

General Editor: Alexander Fenton

MORE FROST AND SNOW

The Diary of Janet Burnet

1758–1795

Edited by
Mowbray Pearson

CANONGATE ACADEMIC
in association with
The European Ethnological Research Centre
and the National Museums of Scotland

Sources in Local History No.2

First published in 1994 by
Canongate Academic, an imprint of Canongate Press Ltd,
14 Frederick Street, Edinburgh EH2 2HB
Copyright © The European Ethnological Research Centre

ISBN 1 898419 08 9

British Library Cataloguing-in-Publication Data
A catalogue record for this book is available on request
from the British Library

Typeset by Falcon Graphic Art Ltd, Wallington, Surrey
Printed and bound by Bookcraft Ltd, Midsomer Norton, Avon

Contents

Transcription of the Diary

Preface

More Frost and Snow was chosen as the title for the review and transcription of the diary of Janet Burnet, because the diary concentrated
very much on the weather which was exceptionally cold and snowy
during the years when the diary was written. It was remarkable not
only that a lady should keep a diary during the second half of the
eighteenth century, but that her principal interest should be in the
weather. Some of the descriptions of the severity of the cold, the
depth of the snow and the vagaries of the weather are fascinating.

Strictly the work is not a true diary in that there is not a record of
the events of each day. At the beginning days, months and even years
are omitted by the author. When the diary becomes more detailed the
events of several days may be summarised and the narrative moves on to
the next entry. However, it qualifies as a diary in so far as it is a continuous account maintained at the time and is not based on reminiscences.

Janet Burnet also took an interest in the effects of the weather
on seedtime and harvest. Those aspects of the diary have been
summarised. She gave some details of the variation in prices of
grain and fodder according to the season.

In many years she closely observed the times of the recurring
natural phenomena, in other words the phenology of the area. Her
findings have been summarised on a monthly basis, so that variations
can be noted year by year.

More about the author, Janet Burnet, will be found in the introduc-
tion, but here it might be of interest to remark that her sister Isabella
was my great, great, great, great grandmother. The diary is by way
of being a family heirloom and I am grateful to her for providing me,
and I hope many others, with a great deal of interest in reading and
studying her record of the past.

I should like to express my thanks to Professor Alexander Fenton of
the European Ethnological Research Centre and the School of Scottish
Studies at Edinburgh University for making possible the publication
of this work.

M.G.Pearson
Juniper Green 1993

Introduction

This diary was written by Janet Burnet (née Dyce), the second wife of George Burnet of Kemnay, Aberdeenshire, whose first wife died in 1750. The first part of the diary from 1758 to 1780 was written at Kemnay House, situated about half a mile to the south west of the village of Kemnay, in the parish of that name, and some eighteen miles by road from Aberdeen. It stands on rising ground at a height of 250 feet (76 metres) above sea level overlooking the valley of the River Don, on the south side of the river. The last entry in that section of the diary was at the end of September 1780, shortly before George Burnet's death on 31st October of that year.

After George Burnet's death, Janet went to live with her sister at Disblair House in the Parish of Fintray, twelve miles from Aberdeen and at a height of 400 feet (122 metres) above sea level. Disblair had been bought in 1744 by Janet's father James Dyce, Merchant in Aberdeen. When he died in 1750 the estate passed to his eldest daughter Agnes who was unmarried. After Janet joined her sister in 1781, they used to spend the summer at Disblair and the winter in Aberdeen. Although the last entry in the diary was 26th August 1795, Janet did not die until 16th July 1802 at the age of 84 and was buried at Kemnay beside her husband. The second, and often more detailed, part of the diary was written at Disblair and Aberdeen. It was evident from the diary that visits were made to Disblair during the winter months, as Mrs Burnet kept closely in touch with events there and elsewhere in the surrounding countryside.

It was obviously the weather that interested Mrs Burnet more than anything else, but she soon showed that she was well aware of its effects on the produce of the garden, the activities on the farm and on the countryside in general.

The first part of the review of the diary examines the highlights of the weather with its effects on farming and other activities during the period at Kemnay from 1758 to 1780 and concludes with a summary of the farming and phenological details observed at Kemnay. The second part covers the years at Disblair and Aberdeen. During that period there was little that could be done by way of analysis and it was felt that the most useful investigation would be that of a comparison between the years on a monthly basis as was done for the time at Kemnay.

Weather and Farming

From 1758 to 1766 some years were omitted and in those years that were covered there were as few as one or two entries for the whole year. In **1762** Janet Burnet began to get the feel of the material that she was to include in her diary when she wrote that *spinag sown that year* was ready on 17th May and that on 16th June she had a *Dish of Peas* also *sown that year* in spite of the fact that on *the 2d April* she had *walked Round a part of Kemnay Parks on the Snow - it being as high as the Dyck and hard & firm to walk on & much Snow over the Ground.*

In **1765** it was the *Exceding hot weather End of July to the 10 August after that Cold as winter with high winds & a stormy sea* which merited a mention in the diary.

It was not until **1766** that details of the weather were given every month. That winter was cold and wet without excesses of either frost or snow. In spring there were late snows in March and April. There were dry spells during a cool summer; thereafter the autumn was dry and frosty. The summary for the year read *This year 80 Days Rain 35 days Snow on the Ground & 17 Days wind.* No indication was given of the strength or direction of the wind on those days, but a strong wind was usually referred to in the diary as a *Loud Wind* which was probably in the order of Beaufort Force 5 or 6 (21 to 28 mph).

There was a very cold start to **1767** with frost and snow during the whole of January and it was not until 19th February that frost and snow were succeeded by wind and rain. Even then there was frost at night. Spring was late again with a good deal of frost & snow in March. Fair weather at the beginning of April was followed by frost, snow and rain towards the end, with wind and more snow at the beginning of May. The summer was cold and wet, with *Rain every day till the last Day which was a Loud Wind.* The autumn was neither excessively cold nor wet. The summary for the year showed that there had been *115 Days of rain 60 days Snow on the Ground 24 days of Wind.*

The year **1768** began with snow and frost with rain at the end of January and again at the end of February. March was anything but spring-like with snow and frost throughout the month. No mention

I

was made of the weather during April, but May was fair with only two days of frost at the beginning of the month. The summer began well with a fair June; July and August were both very wet. The autumn began with fair weather in September, but rain between the 15th and 26th produced *The greatest overflowing of the River Don Ever known.* Winter took over in December with the usual variation between frost, snow and rain. The summary for the year 1768 was the third and last to be given in the diary and recorded *103 days Rain 37 days Snow on the Ground Loud winds 13 days.*

No further entries were made in the diary until **1772** when the adverse weather must have roused Mrs Burnet to action once more. The entry for that year was brief and sufficiently important to be quoted verbatim:

Kemnay 1772 the Storm came on the 6 Jan^r, it lay till the 12 March there was no Blowing & hardly a Day of thaw till the 27 Feb^r when we measurd the Snow it was 20 inches over the whol Ground – this Storm did not go off so as any Plough Could enter the Ground till the 12 of March when the Snow Continowd to Melt till the End of April – never any kindly Thaw but the work went on & Kemnays seed was done the 7th May.

That year was the first in which any activities on the farm were mentioned. In the following year the entry was once more short and to the point:

1773 Jan^r 18 the Mercury fell so Low allmost out of sight the Index could not point it – a pritty Loud wind that Day the 19 Calm – 20 from 8 to 10 o clock a Voilent wind Blowd Down four hundr Trees at Kemnay. No actual readings from the mercury barometer were given in the diary.

Although some snow fell on Christmas Day 1773, it did not start to fall heavily until 1st January **1774**, *when the Snow was very deep.* By the 4th February *this Snow Measurd 14 Inches over all* and then more snow. The thaw came on 12th February & *Continowd to go off Gently without Rain, but we had frost at Night.* It was Mrs Burnet herself who summarised the weather for the remainder of the year:

After this Storm went off, we had not three weeks of dry, or fair, weather till Hervest which was begun the 9 Sept. We had then 3 weeks of fine dry weather, in which time Every Body was so diligent that most of the Crop was got doun & taken in. A few days after, which was the 4th Novr we had Snow but soon went off & Rain came on again & seldom keept off one day till Christmas.

In **1775** the weather throughout January and February was so fine and dry that *Kemnay begun his Oat Seed the first of March.* There had been *no Snow or frost, but for a day or so all the winter.* March was dry and on many days the wind was *so Loud that we Could not go out to walk – Yet the Earth being so Sockd & Beat with the Long Continowance of Rain we had before that there was no Dust Raisd with the Harrows*. The sowing of the Oats was finished on 25th March.

On the following day *Came on a Storm of Snow & hard frost & we filld oor Ice House which Could no be don all winter*. Only one of the two Ice Houses at Kemnay was mentioned on this occasion.

As the result of a warm fortnight in April, *as if June*, the Bear seed was finished on 3rd May and on 6th May the *Peats was Cast*. Thereafter the summer was so hot and dry that the *Crop in General* was *thin & short*. The harvest was begun on 4th August and all was in the yard by 9th September with *all the Rucks Thatchd*. *The weather was so long dry that* they were *Obliged to take the Hors & Cattle to the River of Don to watter them* – but the *Spring that Serves the House* ran *as brisk & full as Ever*.

The weather continued open and fine until 7th January **1776** when the snow returned, fell for three days with no wind and was then *measurd & Computd 14 Inches over all*. In the third week of January two more inches of snow fell and lay until the beginning of February. Ploughing began a week later, but there was still sufficient frost at night to prevent the thawing of the drifted snow. On 15th February more snow meant that *no wheel Carriage Could go from Kemnay to Aberdeen nor any Place Round. This Storm was more severe in England, & was deeper South & North*. Another *great fall of Snow* at the beginning of March was followed by a month of dry, mild weather and the *Oat Seed was don 2d April*. May was a cold month & *kept Back the Grass*, but it was followed by fine, seasonable weather for the whole summer. There was a *fine Crop Especialy of Bear*. The harvest had started on 2nd September and all was in the Yard by 1st October. However there had been a severe frost at the beginning of September which *took off all the Tops of the Petatos* and was *thought to have hurt the Crop in late Low Grounds*.

It was a fine autumn and little sign of winter until the second half of December when the weather became cold and unsettled.

The snow began in earnest on 4th January **1777**. Roads in some parts were impassable and the *Post Could not go* from Stonehaven to Aberdeen. The mail was brought in by three men, *as no Hors Could go*. The depth of snow was *only Computed 4 or 5 Inches*, but they were able to fill their Ice House at this time with ice from the River Don.

On 22nd January there was a brisk thaw, the snow had mostly gone within two days and ploughing began. Throughout February and the first week of March were *fine warm days as if summer*.

During the rest of March frost at night hampered the work in the fields and it was not until 9th April that the *Oat Seed* was *finishd*. The cold weather continued throughout April; on the 20th *the Frost was so Strong that the Watter in the Wilderness was quit Frose over* and on the 30th April *going to Seaton We Could not see out at the Windows of the Chais for snow*. It was cold and wet in May and during June it was so cold that they *could not want a Fire throw out the whole day*.

July and August were both warm and wet; August so wet that there were fears for the hay crop. A dry spell at the end of the month saved the situation and their hay was all got in safely. It was then that *there were two days of Exceding Loud Wind which hurt the Bear when it was well filld or near Rip*.

Fine dry warm weather in September enabled the harvest at Kemnay to begin on the 18th; some of the neighbours had started the week before that. Little enough had been done when, from 7th October, steady rain, with no wind, every day for ten days gave rise to the comment that *nobody Could remember to have seen so much of the Crop Cut doun & all on the Ground at one time*. Eventually shearing was finished on 23rd October and all was *got in* two days later. November was fine and dry, followed by unsettled weather in December.

The first fortnight of January 1778 was *fine pleasant weather* followed by unsettled conditions until the end of February by which time there was enough snow to enable the Ice House to be filled with snow. It was cold enough during the first fortnight of March for the *other Ice House at the top of the Hill* to be filled with ice from *the Watter of Don*.

Rain and snow delayed sowing until 22nd March and the Oat seed was not finished until 2nd April. That was followed by *fine warm weather as in summer till the 13th of April when there came on snow & frost as sever as had been all winter*. Although the ground was *quit hard with frost at 11 o clock forenoon* on the mornings of 23rd and 24th April, the bear seed was finished then.

May and June were both very wet, but the end of June and the beginning of July were characterised by *hot burning weather - not one drop of rain*. New bear meal was eaten on 14th August and a dry month ensured that there was *a good deal Cut doun all round and that there were a good many Bear stacks in the Tennents yards*. As soon as Kemnay's harvest was started on 2nd September the rain came, but from the 6th to the 26th there was no rain to hinder the work which was completed by that date. All was in the yard by 29th September.

The autumn was wet and in November the *River Don rose very high*. On 17th November there was a great deal of thunder and lightning *and all that day was heard in many Places a Noise under Ground or like a Machin driving at a great distance & what the Common Country People Calls Yerd Din.* December was a wet month, but it was exceptionally warm. The *Mavis* was *singing as in summer two at a time.* On the 31st December, however, *there arose such a Voilent wind with Drift along with it that a Man lost his Life going from Kemnay* to Old Rayne & *was found some days after in a place off the Road Calld* Bograxie.

After some more snow on 1st January **1779** there was hard frost and fine sunny days until 17th January. On the following day the *Low Ice House* was filled with ice from the *Watter in the Wilderness.* There were alternate spells of fresh and frost until the end of the month. During February it was such *fine warm Mild Clear Weather* that *any Body might have Sown there Grownd, if they pleased, after the first week of Feb*ʳ. At Kemnay it was thought to be soon enough to start sowing oats on 27th February.

The mild weather continued into March with the result that *the Grass Parks* were *quit Green, & so long that all the young Cattle* were *put on them & out all Night in the feald.* It was also remarked that there was a *Feald of Turnip all in flowr & Yellow all over.* The sowing of oats was finished on 13th March; the remainder of the month was hot and very dry. By the end the *Turnip Park was like a feald of skelly & a vast hight.*

The drought continued into April with hot days, but frost at night. The bear seed was begun on 17th April, but by the 26th there was still no rain. On 29th April there was some snow on the hills and on the 30th there was *a hearty Rain all that afternoon. The Bear Seed was Finished.*

Two cold days at the beginning of May were succeeded by a *heavey fall of Snow* which *by Measuring was Computed 3½ Inches over all. That Morning the Ice House at the Top of the Hill was filld with Snow by the Gardner. The trees was all Loaded with it, as if in the depth of Winter, & it was very Odd looking to see the Honeysuckle & Aple Flowrish Reid, & the Scarlet Cons of the Firs, all Pepping throw the whit Snow.* The snow soon disappeared and the remainder of the month was unsettled.

Two meteorological events in June were described in detail. The first took place on 2nd June when *sitting by the watter in the Wilderness we seed a Piller of Watter Rise as high as the talest Tree & fall doun again, after which it Rolld along for a Considerable space in large Rolls, as if a Vast Cask had been under the Watter, & out of those Rolls, sprung up smal strins of Watter, Rising pritty high, as out of the Strup of a Razer – The Noise it Made was such as a fire work of Powder makes when first set off, but much Louder – The Day was Clear, fine sune shine & not a <u>Breath of Wind.</u>*

The warm, sultry weather in June favoured such tornado-like phenomena. On 16th June on the way to Aberdeen Mrs Burnet described how she saw *a Pillar of Dust Rise in the Road before us a little – which seemed Round & solid as high as a House & from that mounted up in smok, as high as the Eye Could see it. When we Came up to the place we could see no mark it had made in the Road.*

On 19th June it was *as Cold as Winter with showrs of Rain & Snow & Hail.* Three days later the Ice House that had been filled in January was opened and it was found to be *quit full of Ice.*

From 2nd to 9th July the *hottest weather anyone remembers* was followed by severe thunderstorms during which two men and two horses were killed some miles from Aberdeen on the Banchory road. For the next ten days the weather was *Excessive Hot, not like oor Climat.* On 20th July the *Ice House that was filld the 3ᵈ of May* was opened and the snow was found to be in *much the same state as when put in, but it froze the Cream very well.*

The entry on 26th July read as follows: *from 11 o clock to 2 o clock forenoon we had the Most tremindeous Storm of Thunder & Lightning Ever Rememberd here accompanyd with Large Hail & heavy Rain. At Kintor, the Lightning Came doun a Vent of three Chimneys & struck a Maid on the Leg & a Dog Killd, but she only fealt it numbd for soome Hours – at Clunie & Monymusk several people fealt the same.*

After more rain at the beginning of August, the remainder of the month was very warm and dry. As early as 13th August harvest was begun, but only the *Men servants* were employed until the 23rd when the crop was fully ripe and *all hands* were *set to work.* Apart from a few light showers at the beginning of September the weather remained dry enough for the harvest to be finished on 15th September and two days later all the stacks were thatched.

October was a fine month, but the ground was still so dry that in many parts no ploughing was possible. A real change in the weather did not come until 14th November when the hills were covered with snow and there was snow on the lower ground during the following two days. There was more snow towards the end of the month and the frost was so hard that *they were walking oor the River Don on the Ice.* On 28th November the River Don rose very high when there was heavy rain and the ice melted. In December the weather was unsettled, with a mixture of snow and rain.

At the beginning of January **1780** the snow lay deep on the hills and the temperatures dropped as the month proceeded. Many things in the house froze *amongst others a Large jar of Duble Distilld Pepermint Water in the Garret but not near a Window.* On 15th January the *Low*

Ice House was filld with Ice from the watter in the Garden. The other Ice House was filled on 23rd January as the cold weather continued with occasional showers of snow, but *the Snow* was *not 2 Inches deep & fine walking.*

At the end of the first week of February it was remarked that horses and carts had been able to cross the River Don on the ice for several weeks and it was not until there was a rapid thaw on 17th February that the river *broke.* Further falls of snow with a thaw to follow did not interfere unduly with the ploughing which began on the last day of the month.

Strong winds characterised the whole of March with occasional showers of snow. The sowing of oats began on 14th March and was completed on the 29th. It had been interrupted on the 18th by *a dunright Hurican of wind the whol day & night.*

There was a cold start to the month of April with strong frost and, on 3rd April, heavy snow. Cold weather with snow and rain continued throughout the month and delayed the work on the farm. By the end of the month there were *no parks of Grass looking Green, the work was going very Slowly on & no Bear sown yet.* In many places the sowing of oats was not nearly finished.

A week of warm weather at the beginning of May enabled the work to go on *Briskly.* The bear seed was finished on 12th May and the *Grass & every thing made great progress.* On 19th May the hills were again covered with snow and the warmer weather did not return until the end of the month. The first week of June was warm and dry, but on the night of the 6th and the *three following* there was *such sever Frost that the Ice was on the Pools in the Morning . . . and many things Visibly destroyed.* In general both June and July were cold and wet.

A dry and hot August, *as hot as any weather all last summer,* enabled *the Hervest begun Round Kemnay to be Constant the 20th of August.* On the following day the *Low Ice House* was opened & *had Plenty of Ice.* The harvest at Kemnay itself began on 28th August during hot, dry weather and was finished on 23rd September with *all got in to the Yard* five days later.

At that point the diary at Kemnay ended and was not resumed until September 1781 at Disblair House. From the above account at Kemnay the following tables have been compiled, showing the effects of the weather on the farming year:

	SEEDTIME		HARVEST
	Oats	*Bear*	
1772		– 7 May	
1774			9 Sept – 30 Sept
1775	1 – 25 March	– 3 May	4 Aug – 9 Sept
1776		– 2 Apr	2 Sept – 1 Oct
1777		– 9 Apr	18 Sept – 25 Oct
1778	22 Mar – 2 Apr	– 24 Apr	2 Sept – 29 Sept
1779	27 Feb – 13 Mar	17 Apr – 30 Apr	13 Aug – 17 Sept
1780	14 Mar – 29 Mar	2 May – 12 May	28 Aug – 28 Sept

Table 1 - Dates for the beginning and ending of sowing and of harvest 1772 – 1780.

	SEEDTIME	HARVEST	TOTAL (SEED TO YARD)
1774		3	
1775	9	5	28 weeks
1776		4	
1777		5	
1778	5	4	27
1779	9	5	29
1780	9	4	28

Table 2 – Length of time in weeks for seedtime, harvest and the whole period of activity on the farm from the sowing of the first seeds to the completion of the stacks in the yard.

In spite of the vagaries of the weather described in the diary, the figures in the above tables remained remarkably constant. The harvest of 1774 was completed very quickly. A late spring in 1778 delayed seedtime until 22nd March, but the work was completed in five weeks and the harvest was not much later than usual.

The principal crops associated with the harvest at Kemnay were hay, oats and bear. Although the root crops mentioned were potatoes and turnips, little mention was made of any work associated with the cultivation of either.

Livestock included horses and cattle; bees were kept and swarms were noted. Little was said about any of the activities on the farm, apart from those mentioned so far. However, Mrs Burnet did pay close attention to the ways in which the trees, the flowers and the garden produce responded to seasonal variations of the weather. These are now summarised by months for the years between 1758 and 1780, together with some of the agricultural details already given, for the sake of comparison.

Phenological and Agricultural Details

JANUARY

1777 **24** Ploughing begun.

1779 **24** Fine mild weather and the mavis singing strongly.

FEBRUARY

1776 **8** Ploughing begun.

1779 Cherry plum in full flower.

27 Sowing oats begun.

1780 **28** Ploughing begun.

MARCH

1772 **12** Ploughing begun. No ploughing earlier owing to severe snowstorms.

1775 **1** Sowing of oats begun following fine dry spell.

25 Sowing of oats completed.

1779 **7** Grass parks quite green; young cattle put out on them; left out at night. Rose bushes, gooseberry bushes and some hawthorns were all green.

13 Sowing of oats completed.

16 & 17 Days as warm as June or July. Standard cherry plum white all over with blossom. Some blossom on other plums; a good deal of pear blossom out.

24 Pears and plums white all over. Leaf of *plain* tree *quit expanded*.

30 Cherries and damsons in full blossom. A good deal of apple blossom and flowers on strawberries.

1780 **14** Sowing of oats begun.

29 Sowing of oats completed.

APRIL

1776 **2** Sowing of oats completed. *Trees most remarkably full flowrished & every shrub beautiful. Firs & every tree loaded with seed.*

1777 **9** Sowing of oats completed.

1778 **2** Sowing of oats completed.

24 Bear seed all sown in spite of snow and frost during the month.

1779 **4** Birch leaves *penny broad*. Some of the geans at Kemnay were in blossom; the old ones at Castle Fraser were almost over. Peas in flower.

13 Pears set as big as peas and cherry plums even larger.

17 Sowing of bear seed begun.

20 Cherries well advanced and strawberries in full flower. A good deal of *seed* on the firs and on all the trees.

30 Sowing of bear seed completed.

1780 **14** Cherry plum on the wall in blossom and pear blossom pretty far on.

27 No grass parks looking green and no trees except the larch. Work going slowly. No bear seed sown in many places nor sowing of oats finished.

MAY

1758 **21** Spinach cut, sown that year. Peas in flower.

1762 **17** Spinach cut, sown that year, although on 2 April the snow had been as high as the dyke and hard & firm to walk on.

1772 **7** Bear seed all sown.

14 *had a large Cukember.*

1775 **3** Sowing of bear completed.

6 Peats cast.

9 Honeysuckle in full flower.

1776 Cold month with frost and wind which destroyed most of the plums and pears. Growth of grass was retarded.

26 A *Cukember* cut.

1778 A wet month with good growth of grass, but crop on low grounds showing signs of damage from heavy rain.

1779 **3** Heavy snowfall to depth of 3½ inches. Honeysuckle, apple blossom and *Scarlet Cons of the Firs all Pepping throw the whit Snow.*

8 First salad at table - cucumber and young turnip.

26 Dish of turnips.

29 Some pods of green peas, which were in flower at the beginning of April, were quite full, but all the rest of them were ruined by the frost and snow. The peas sown in March were in flower and would be ready before the others.

1780 **1 - 8** Grass and braird appearing. Leaves on one plane tree quite expanded, but not one birch leaf *penny broad*.

11 A good deal of blossom out.

12 Sowing of bear seed completed.

15 All fruit trees in full blossom. Grass and crops making good progress.

JUNE

1758 **18** Dish of peas; some cherries and strawberries.

1760 **11** Dish of green peas.

1768 **18** Green peas. Cherries and strawberries several times before 29.

1775 **10** Dish of green peas.

1777 *No appearance of fruit of any kind this year, & no seed on the firs, or on any tree.*

1778 Still wet. *A great deal of Flowrish but Late.*

1779 **2** Cabbage at table.

    15 A dish of cherries.

    22 A dish of green peas. Strawberries.

1780 **6** Salad and *Cukember*

    28 First melon cut - good crop. Also cucumbers.

JULY

1765 **3** Green peas and artichokes. Strawberries and cherries just beginning.

1766 **8** Green peas and strawberries ready.

    12 Cherries ripe.

1777 **10** A few strawberries ready.

1778 **20** First shower of rain since 23 June.

1779 **19** Plums ripe at Gordon Castle. Early variety of apricots finished and later variety ready for eating.

1780 **20** Peas, strawberries and cherries all ready for eating.

AUGUST

1775 **4** Harvest begun.

1777 **12** Wet month; hay crop in danger. Hay all got in safely at Kemnay by end of month.

1778 **14** Fresh bear meal eaten.

    26 Fine warm weather continued. Good deal of grain cut; bear stacks in tenants' yards.

1779 **13** Harvest begun by menservants only.

    23 All hands set to work.

    27 Pears and apples all ripe and falling off

1780 **20** Harvest begun in Kemnay district.

    28 Harvest begun at Kemnay.

SEPTEMBER

1774 **9** Harvest begun. Most of crop *got doun & taken in* in three weeks.

1775 **9** Harvest completed and ricks thatched. Weather so dry that horses and cattle had to be watered at River Don.

1776 **2** Harvest begun. A night's frost that *took off all the Tops of the Petatos* was thought to have hurt the crop in the *late Low Grounds*.

1777 **18** Harvest begun.

1778 **2** Harvest begun at Kemnay.

6 No progress; rain every day.

29 Harvest completed; everything in stackyard.

1779 **15** Harvest finished.

17 Stacks thatched.

1780 **23** Harvest finished at Kemnay.

28 All in the yard. Good fruit year. Surplus of geans; some gooseberries and apples sold.

OCTOBER

1776 **1** Harvest completed.

There was a good crop of bear. Fruit was plentiful, with a glut of apples. Pears were affected by the early frost in September and would not keep.

1777 **7** Only one small field cut and one small stack of bear got in. Very little work was done for the next ten days. Heavy rain and no wind. *Nobody Could remember to have seen so much of the Crop Cut doun & all on the ground at one time.*

18 A good deal of the bear and corn taken in.

23 Shearing finished.

25 Harvest finished.

1779 **28** Ground too dry and hard for ploughing in many parts. Fruit not keeping well. Even the *Nonsuch and other "keeping" apples were rotting.*

NOVEMBER

1779 During the autumn many trees had as much blossom as they had in spring.

14 The fruit set and some apples, as large as a small golden pippin, were picked.

DECEMBER

1778 First fortnight wet, but unusually mild - *not like winter weather. The mavis singing as in summer.*

During the last three years at Kemnay the diary became more detailed and that characteristic, especially with regard to the weather, was continued when the journal was resumed at Disblair. It was possible to ascertain how seedtime, haymaking and harvest varied from year to year (Tables 3 and 4).

For the principal topics noted in the diary such as the weather, events on the farm and seasonal variations within the garden and on the estate, the following summary provides a comparison between those events recounted by Mrs Burnet each month over the years.

It should be remembered that during the winter months, usually from November to April, Mrs Burnet and her sister lived in Aberdeen where the diary was then written. However, some references were made to events that were taking place in the country in general and at Disblair in particular.

JANUARY

1782 Unsettled with frost and snow, but little on the ground.

1783 **18 & 19** *a great deal of Snow with Blowing & sever Frost, which Stopt all traveling with wheel carriges for some days*
    24 Thaw till end of month.

1784   **2** *at Night a most Voilent Storm of wind at South East - this Hurrican of Wind Blowd all the Snow into Such Wreaths as was never Seen in this Country Many of them 18 foot perpindicular. Many People was two Days in there Houses befor they Could be Cast so as to let them out.*

    3 *Many Houses in the Country was unroofd & Stacks of Corn & Hay Carried off.*

    31 *The frost was most remarkable the Thermometr fell 5½ degrees below the frizing point - roots of all kinds was froze, Bear in Cask & bottle Large jars of Pepermint Watter all most all, House flowr roots*

& Plants was Killd it only Continowd So intence for 20 or 24 Hours So very Sever.

1785   **1** Snow very deep in the country, but little in Aberdeen.

      12 Fresh, open weather for remainder of month.

      29 Some oats sown and potatoes planted near Aberdeen.

1786   **1** *A great deal of Snow, the Storm very deep.*

      2 & 3 *a more intence Frost Meat Roots & Milk Froze hard.*

      6 *In the Country they have thought this Storm more Sever & the Frost Stronger then it was at any time the two by past winters. By the Storm of wind many Ships have been lost on this Coast.*

      15 *Strong frost & more Snow which is now very deep.*

      21 to end of month *Fine open Blowing weather. Some days as warm as Summer, all work going on Briskly in the Country the ground dry.*

1787 Mild weather throughout the month.

1788   **3** *Warm like summer.*

      13 Frost and snow.

1789   **2 to 8** *Soft Mild Air with Rain almost every day.*

      10 *Snow & very Cold.*

      13 Unsettled - fresh and frost to end of month.

1790   **1 to 10** Dry, open weather – a great deal of the ploughing done.

1791   **1 to 14** Cold, wet and windy – *the Ploughing in the Country much kept Back.*

      14 to 31 Strong winds with rain and snow.

1792 Rain at beginning and end of month with snow from **9 to 22** – *all to the South & in the Country the frosts have never Brok nor the Snow – at any time Lying 2 Inch deep, & no work don Since Nov*.

1793 A cold month with a great deal of rain.

1794   **1** *Strong frost Snow in the Hills.*

      9 to 19 *Open fresh weather hardly any frost all the Grass Green as Summer & a great Blow of flowrs in the Garden.*

      24 *a heavy fall of Snow (the first Snow we have Seen all this winter).*

      29 *No Post for 4 days.*

      31 *a Brisk wind with thaw.*

1795 Unsettled frost and fresh until **23** *the frost greater then We have Seen for many years – the Storm deep in the Country.*

      27 *a great deal of Snow – the fly for Edin^r Could get no further then Stonhive.*

      31 *Stron frost & non of the Snow gon.*

FEBRUARY

1782 **14** *The Snow computed 8 Inches over all,* after a fortnight of snowfall, which lasted for another week.

22 Thaw began; a good deal of rain, but cold.

28 *Snow in the Hills little melted.*

1783 **2** *Some Plughing got don, but much of the Snow lying &* Bad traveling.

9 Snow and rain in Aberdeen, *but all Snow in the Country.*

23 Dry with strong wind; *so sever a Frost as to stop Plughing.*

28 Mild and snow melting a little during the day.

1784 **7** *Still a More heavey fall of Snow & Cold wind.*

This Snow Blown in new wreath by the wind that was along with it made traveling Still worce then ever, & Except the South Post Road there is no way a Wheel Machin Can go – the wind all this Storm has kept so much to the North that few Ships Could get from the South here, which has made Coals almost not to be got & has destressed the poor excedingly.

1785 Snow at the beginning of the month followed by alternate frost and fresh until **17th February**.

20 & 21 *Still more snow; the Storm deeper than it has been all winter, but Coals Cheap & plenty.*

22 & 23 *Strong Frost & Showrs of Snow - all traveling to the North in any wheel Machin impossible.*

1786 Unsettled with alternate rain and snow.

1787 **7** Oats sown near Aberdeen.

24 Spring flowers in full bloom. Gooseberry and currant leaves almost expanded. Blossom buds on trees far advanced. Many people sowing near Aberdeen.

1788 **9** Ground always so wet that little labouring done.

28 Good deal of snow in the country. No ploughing since 18th February.

1789 **2** *a fine warm day as much so as summer.*

Open weather for most of the month.

1790 **5 to 23** Warm, open weather. Everything coming on fast. Fields green all winter - now looking like May.

1791 **3** Great deal of snow and hard frost – *we have not seen so much Snow this 18 months.*

10 to 22 Rain and wind with *the most voilent Storm of wind we have yet heard* on **22nd**. Strong frost at end of month.

1792 First week cold, followed by open weather and more frost at end of month

1793 Unsettled – strong winds and rain; occasional cold spells.
1794 Rain and strong winds with snow and frost on **10th and 11th**.
1795 Very heavy snow and severe frost throughout the month.

MARCH

1781 **15** Sowing of Oats finished in Disblair district.
1783 **18** Oats sown at Disblair.
1784 **21** After a long winter of snow, ploughing begun in many places.
1785 **8** No work done since **29th January**.
 20 Thaw at last. Ploughing begun.
1786 **11** *the frost so sever as to put stop for some time past to all work. this day in the afternoon we had a Showr of Snow the flakes So Large as few People has ever Seen.*
 Remainder of month cold and unsettled.
1787 **17** Oat seed begun at Disblair. Everybody sowing.
 22 Some apple blossom out. Hawthorn *pretty green*. Currants and gooseberries *quit green* and in flower.
1788 **22** *No work has been done in the Country all this time in the fealds or Gardens.* (Snow).
 31 Since 22 heavy drizzling weather. No work done and no seeds sown.
1789 First week showers of snow and rain.
 9 *a great fall of Snow & Blowing. 12 a foot depth of more Snow.*
 13 *more Snow wind & frost.*
 31 *a good fall of Snow.* Great accumulation of snow during the month.
1790 **1** Still mild. Oat seed started.
 12 Oat seed almost finished in most places.
 21 Blossom on some apples almost out; pears far advanced.
1791 **14** Everyone beginning to sow.
 25 Sowing going on everywhere.
 28 Oat seed done at Disblair and neighbourhood.
1792 **19** In some parts begun to sow.
 22 Begun to sow oat seed at Disblair.
1794 **16** Everybody beginning to sow now.
 20 to 26 Fine dry days – sowing going ahead – some people finished oats.
1795 **20** After a very cold and snowy winter, *some ploughing going on, but none in the Country.*
 22 *Some parks near Aberdeen sown with oats.*
 26 Ploughing begun at Disblair. Sowing in many parts. Far hills still covered with snow.

APRIL

1781   **23** *the Plain Tree & Hors Chesnut - Some Leaves quit expanded.*

1782   **1** Sowing of oats begun at Aberdeen - also some field peas.

8 Left Aberdeen for Disblair. Very little ploughing done and hardly any seed sown in Disblair district.

18 Sowing proceeding very slowly - Snow and cold.

20 No sign of growth – *all as winter.*

21 A great deal sown during the past week. No leaves on the trees - not even the gooseberry bushes showing any sign of leaf.

24 All low ground sown, and most of the sowing completed around Disblair. In many other places little done.

30 The peas which had just been showing above ground on **8th** April were not yet half an inch above ground. Not one gooseberry bush in full leaf, nor had any of the buds on the trees opened. Blossom ready to burst given one warm day.

1783   **1** Great activity sowing everywhere. Grass greener than at the end of April 1782. All sowing, except the low ground, finished at Disblair. Some spring flowers out and the gooseberries showing leaf.

9 Low ground sown

12 *Began to sow the Bear park.* The grass looking green and some fields of oats green. Plum blossom out. Gooseberry bushes in leaf. Sowing of oats finished in most parts.

19 Larch quite green. Gooseberries, currants and raspberries in leaf. Pear blossom fully out. Buds on the birch green.

20 *at Fintray young Latice of this years sowing & Radish at Table. Peas of this year Stringd & will be soon in Blosom, French Beans far advanced. Cherrie Trees in full Blowsom – the Buds of the Plain Tree Burst & Showing there Leaf tho not Expanded.*

29 Bear seed finished in the park.

1784   **12** No sign of vegetation during the drive from Aberdeen to Disblair. At Disblair a few crocuses and some spring flowers. Some peas sown before winter above ground.

19 Some peas and oats sown.

20 Sowing continuing when ground dry, but very little done yet.

28 Remainder of Oats sown at Disblair. Everybody now sowing if possible *Throw dispair.* Potatoes planted at Disblair.

1785   **11** Sowing Oats at Disblair after interruptions by snow and frost.

14 *Came to Disblair. A good deal Sowed everywhere.* Spring flowers in *great glory.* Peas sown that year above ground. Larch buds looking green. Some pear blossom far advanced.

17 Oat seed finished at Disblair.

24 Oat seed finished in many places.

25 Potatoes planted.

1786 **1** Many places some oats sown.

6 Some oats sown at Disblair.

20 *Came to Disblair.* Larch begun to look green. Peas and apple blossom pretty well advanced, but not out. Spring flowers out. Peas sown before winter above ground and those sown in spring about the same.

1787 **12** *Came to Disblair.*

14 and 15 Gooseberries and currants in leaf and flower. Some peas and cherry blossom out. Leaves on some plane trees *expanded*. Hardly any birch buds green. Larch green and cones on young trees. Spring flowers in great glory. Grass well on, but damaged by frost and cold weather.

26 Breird and grass looking well. Things in garden looking well, *but little advanced since we came here.*

1788 **16** *Came to Disblair,* where oat seed begun on **14th**. Very little vegetation. *Greens and plants in the Garden all taken off.* Gooseberries pretty green and blossom buds on trees beginning to swell. Spring flowers *in blow*. Larch beginning to show green.

27 Oat seed at Disblair finished. Some pear and cherry blossom expanded. Grass looking very green.

29 Bear seed begun. *the Leaf of the Young Plain Tree Expanded.*

1789 **13** Oat seed begun at Disblair

22 Mostly finished. *Every thing looking very Blick. the Larch just beginning to Look Green. Currans on the Wall in Flowrish & the Flowrish of some Plumbs to look whit. Gooseberries in Leaf.*

1790 **20** *Came to Disblair.* Oat breird green, but hurt by the weather as also the grass. Larch and hawthorn green. *Junkels & Single Narsses Blown & the Enemones in full Blow, but all looking very poorly. Pears in full Flowrish & a good deal on the Aple Trees, but all looks as droping off.*

21 Begun bear seed.

1791 **3** Oat seed everywhere finished.

25 *got Hyaunths and duble Polyanthus Narsiss - & all the difrent kinds of Spring flowrs in full Blow from Disblair.*

1792 **6** Oat seed finished at Disblair.

12 In Aberdeen hawthorn and gooseberry bushes green. Pear blossom just bursting.

24 *Came to Disblair.* Everything as far advanced as when Janet Burnet came out on **10th May** 1791.

1793 **14** Very little of the oat seed in the ground.

1794 **3** Oats finished in most places.

30 *Came to Disblair.*

1795 **9** After heavy rain and melting snow the River Don rose *7 feet perpendicular. All work in the Country put a stop to.*

MAY

1781 **1** Leaves of plane and horse chestnut trees fully out.

16 Bear seed finished.

24 Spinach cut. Plenty of radishes ready. Strawberries in flower.

31 Peas in flower. Hawthorn, laburnum and rowans in flower.

1782 **11** In many places oat seed not sown.

12 Some cherry plum and apple blossom out. Some larches looking green and the grass looking better. Gooseberry bushes *not fully leafd yet.*

21 and 22 Bear seed being sown.

23 *not a Bud burst on any Forest Tree, but the Larch.*

26 *Plain Tree Buds opend & Some Leaves on the Hathorn – little Flowrish on the Fruit Trees.*

28 Sowing of bear seed finished in most places, though hardly begun in others.

1783 **1** Larch fully out. Hawthorn green and leaves of many plane trees quite expanded. Pears, plums, apples and cherries on the wall in blossom. Grass and *braird* looking fine. Gooseberries and currants in leaf and flower.

9 Bear seed finished at Disblair, with grass seed sown and rolled.

21 Large *Sallet* at table. Blossom on peas, pears and apples. All trees, except ash, in full leaf and glory. Gooseberries and currants netted.

24 Severe frost took off tops of potatoes.

1784 **1** No blossom yet. Some leaves beginning on the gooseberries. Not a larch changed colour. Not a bud green on birch or hawthorn.

5 Lint sown. Ground wonderfully dried and everything making great progress.

6 First of bear at Disblair sown.

9 Cuckoo heard for first time. Everybody, except in *hill touns*, finished sowing oats - now concentrating on bear. Some oat *breer* showing. Grass looking green. Larch far advanced. Gooseberry bushes almost fully leafed and some pear blossom out.

16 Lint above ground. Oat breer looking well. Grass good. Larch *in high glory*. Birch leaves *penny broad*. Beech, Elm, Hawthorn and some Plane trees out. Blossom on plum, cherry, apple and pear on wall.

22 Most of bear seed sown and a great deal above ground.

26 All trees now in full leaf and ash pretty well on.

1785 **1** Good deal of bear sown at Disblair. Gooseberries and currants in full leaf and flower. Plum, cherry, pear and apple blossom out. Leaf on young birch *near penny broad*. All larch pretty green.

21 *Bear parks done*. Grass sown and rolled. Sowing of bear mostly finished everywhere.

30 *a Sellat with Radish &c at Table some days ago.*

1786 **1** Gooseberry bushes and currants in full leaf and flower. Some cherry, plum, apple and pear blossom white. Great deal of breer up and looking green. Everyone busy on bear land.

19 Larch *in high glory*. Some young plane leaves expanded. Blossom on wall trees almost fully out, but not on standards. Sowing of bear far advanced.

20 Disblair finished bear sowing. Grass sown and rolled.

28 Beech and plane just out; also hawthorn and rowan. Birch not more than *penny broad*. Wall trees in full blossom. Strawberries in flower. Salad with radish at table.

1787 **2** *this storm & long Cold weather has taken off all the out feald Grass.*

7 Began sowing bear seed. Plane tree in full leaf. Plums and pears *in full flurish, some Blown flurish on the Gins - & a Standard Pear Tree. the Birch not penny Broad yet.*

16 Birch now *penny broad*. All trees, except oak and ash, leaves expanded. Strawberries in *full Flowrish & the Currans & goosberries knotted. Radish often at Table*. Bear seed finished. Cherries as big as small peas. Damsons and *gins* (geans) all white with blossom.

1788 **9** Strawberries in flower. Larch in high glory.

11 Snow, hail, high wind and frost. Bear breer all taken off. Many things hurt in the garden.

16 Birches penny broad. Plane, hawthorn and many other trees in leaf.

19 Milder. Some cherries set. Apples (except standards), geans. pears and plums in full blow.

22 Bear seed finished.

29 Cherries as big as geans. Currants and gooseberries very forward. Peas in *full Blosom*. Rowan and laburnum in flower. Leaves of the young ash expanded. Pears and apples set.

30 Gooseberries large enough for tarts.

1789 **2** Bear seed begun.

15 Bear seed well on in that area. Plane and horse chestnut leaves expanded. Birch penny broad. Pears and plums in full blossom.

1790 **13** Bear seed parks finished. Some of young birches now penny broad, but many of old ones like winter. Rowan and chestnut showing leaves. Strawberries in flower. Some young geans in flower.

24 Geans in full flower. Peas in flower. Birch may now be said to be all penny broad.

1791 **10** *Came to Disblair*. All trees in high glory. Many birches penny broad. Some plane trees in full leaf – all mostly so except ash. Pear and apple blossom out. Cherry and plum on the wall, but no blossom on standard trees.

25 After cold, wet month, grass and breer much yellowed.

1792 **29** Trees of all kinds full of blossom and setting. Gean flowers mostly shaken. Peas and strawberries in full flower. Salad ready. Currants and gooseberries like small peas, but all fallen off and *the Stalks mostly quit Stript*. All the trees in full glory, except the ash, but it was sad to see so much damage caused by the weather.

1793 **2** *Came to Disblair*. Everything very backward. Oat seed finished, but bear not started. Apples not nearly in leaf. No green on any forest tree. Some pear blossom, but very little.

9 A great deal of bear seed done.

11 Our bear seed finished.

15 Bear seed mostly finished.

16 All trees in pretty full foliage, except the ash. Birch penny broad.

23 Blossom out on all trees on wall.

26 A cucumber cut.

1794 **3** Bear seed finished. Larch in high glory. Birch penny broad. Elm and other trees, except ash, far advanced. Trees on wall in blossom. Currants and gooseberries set. Flowers in full blow including hyacinths in open ground. Rain much wished for.

14 Peas in flower.

15 Large cucumber and radish at table.

1795 **1** Oat seed not yet finished in many places. Ground wet.

30 *Came out to Disblair*. Trees full of blossom and all trees in leaf except the old ash. Everything looking better than expected after such wet weather. Grass and breer a little yellowed.

JUNE

1781   **30** Poor hay crop after a cold wet month. Large dish of green peas and dish of strawberries. Some cherries ripe.

1782   **9** No tree yet in full leaf, though plane, elm. birch and laburnum had some leaves. No blossom on standard fruit trees. A little more blossom on the pears and apples on the wall than there had been on 28th May. Cherry blossom fully out, but nothing else making progress. Some grass very poor and natural grass not growing at all. Sowing of bear not nearly finished.

15 Gean in full bloom. Strawberries, pears and apples fully blown; also plums on the wall and one standard pear tree. Spinach ready.

22 All trees now in full leaf except the ash. Some cherries set and some pears on the wall. Some gooseberries the size of peas. Standard apples not in blossom yet, except the Oslen.

26 Standard trees in full blossom. Peas in full flower.

1783   **14** Small turnips ready for eating. Gooseberries for tarts. Ash tree in leaf.

1784   **2** Blossom on standard trees. Gean and trees on wall losing their blossom – fruit setting. Cherries quite large. Peas that came through the winter now in flower. In some places bear seed not yet finished.

7 Peas in full flower.

20 Leaves of peas speckled with frost. Spinach several times at table. Salad ready. Foliage of trees damaged by frost.

28 Turnip seed finished

1785   **9** Grass looking ill. Little fruit set. Ash hardly in leaf.

11 Peas in full bloom

18 Turnips sown.

1786   **7** All trees now in full glory. Laburnum and rowan in flower. Standard fruit trees in blossom. Strawberries and first row of peas in flower. Ash fully out for most part.

25 A few strawberries ripe.

26 First rain since 13th May.

1787   **4** Rowan, laburnum and hawthorn in full flower. Ash leaves pretty well out. Standard tree in full blossom - blossom on pears. French beans well on.

10 Following frost and snow, *Everything Exceedingly hurt the French Beans quit taken off & all Potatos above Ground the Larch quit Broun & the young Shoots of many of the Spruce*

Firs the Leaf of the Ash now pretty fare advanced. All like Dulce.

27 Gooseberry pie and young turnips at table.

1788 **2** Salad at table.

12 Spinach at table. Very little fruit set. Hay exceedingly short and all shot - dried and yellow in some places. Green gooseberries at table. Fruit not swelling and dropping off.

24 Green peas ready. Bees swarmed. Some ripe strawberries and cherries.

30 Second swarm of bees.

1789 **1** All trees, except ash, now in full foliage. Geans and all kinds of plums white all over. Strawberries in flower. Pears, gooseberries and currants set.

24 Cold season. Some peas in flower. Little appearance of any fruit set, though trees had been loaded with blossom.

30 Nothing in garden made any progress during the past ten days. Constant East winds – North or South-East for past two months. Fruit trees looking as if burnt and foliage of all trees much hurt.

1790 **13** Ash just out, but its leaves and those of other trees much hurt by frost.

23 Tasted a few strawberries and green peas.

1791 **1** Warm like summer. Peas in flower. Geans losing their blossom. Standard trees in full blossom. Pears on wall set.

1792 **24** Nothing advanced in past eight days. Peas in pods not swelling. Clover blackened with frost.

1793 **8** Cut two melons. Gooseberries and currants like small peas. Some pears set.

17 Cold spell. Frost at night. All gooseberries and currants dropped off the bushes.

19 Strong, cold winds. All the geans, damsons &c shaken off the trees.

1794 **17** Gooseberries ready for baking. *Eat some Peas out of the Pod in the Garden.*

24 Dish of green peas, some new potatoes & a melon at table.

1795 **3** Great deal of gean flower blown down.

15 Peas in full flower. Spinach.

JULY

1781 **18** Cutting hay ripened for seed

1782 **1** Laburnum, rowan, lilac and hawthorn in full flower. Grass much improved.

14 Hay crop very good.

24 Plenty of strawberries and green peas ready. Also turnip.

29 Cabbage at table.

1783   **7** Some strawberries eaten. Green peas twice at table - also artichokes. Turnip often.

17 Hay cut.

29 A little bear cut.

1784   **9** Hay all cut at Disblair. Second sowing of turnip necessary and in many places turnips sown three times.

17 Peas, strawberries and artichokes at table. (In Aberdeen strawberries eaten on 14th July, but scarce and not very ripe).

22 Cabbage at table.

1785   **2** Peas, cabbage and baked gooseberries at table - also young turnips. Strawberries and cherries tasted.

12 Hay cut. All the bear shot.

29 Potatoes at table.

1786 **12** Hay in tramp coles.

22 Hay in sow.

1787   **3** Begun to cut hay.

5 (First day without a fire). Tasted strawberries, cherries and a few green peas. Bees swarmed.

9 Some hay in coles, but mostly as cut.

10 and 11 All hay in pretty large coles.

17 Crop in good ground looking well. Good deal of bear shot. Oat fields and low ground looking poorly.

18 Dry. Some hay got into yard.

20 Green peas at table. Cherries and strawberries for second time. A second swarm of bees.

23 All hay got into the Corn Yard.

1788   **1** *Hay greatly mended*. Fruit swelling. Everything much recovered by the rain. Plenty of peas. Artichokes at table.

4 Began to cut hay.

6 The park cut.

7 Put in coles.

14 Hay got into Yard in large tramp coles before rain came.

20 and 21 Began to cut hay kept for seed.

26 Hay threshed and into the Yard.

1789   **4** Began to cut hay. 16 Cherries, strawberries and a *whap* or two of green peas tasted.

18 Hay all cut, but in a sad state *here and every where &* *a good crop there is.*

20 Got some of the hay in small cocks.

21 First fair day *from end to end*. First day without *fogg* since 20th June.

27 Peas and strawberries at table.

29 Plenty of peas and strawberries now.

1790 **8** Cherries and strawberries *in Plenty where there is Plenty, but that in very few Places. The Large Fruit will be Scarce Everyway.* Everyone cutting hay.

9 Hay at Disblair cut. Hay generally pretty good. Bear and oats on good ground looking well, but in general thin and short.

16 Rain since 9th July. Hay much the worse and like to rot.

1791 **11** Cabbage and turnip at table. Not a strawberry ready yet. Began to cut hay. Crop not as good as usual.

16 Tasted strawberries and some pods of green peas are pretty full. Bear shot in many places.

18 Hay all in tramp coles in the Corn Yard.

22 Strawberries and peas in plenty.

1792 **16** Peas at table. Began to cut hay.

24 Hay in the Corn Yard in large tramp coles. Turnip, potatoes and strawberries at table.

26 *Not one Day this whole Summer that could be calld very Hott - & often a touch of frost throw the whole yet the Crop looks well and most of the Bear Shot.*

1793 **15** Turnip and small carrot at table. Cabbage well started a fortnight ago. Not one strawberry - no peas ready.

18 Cut the hay - a very poor crop.

25 Some peas at table and some strawberries ready.

1794 **5** Dry, hot weather continued. Feared turnip all gone off.

6 Beans, peas and strawberries now in plenty.

19 Still dry and hot. Bear crop turning yellow and many grass parks like stubble after harvest.

1795 **2** Not a strawberry set, but plants full of flowers. Every tree and shrub full of flowers this year. Hawthorn white all over.

13 Turnip and new potatoes at table. A ripe strawberry to be seen for a wonder.

21 Fruit not *Sweeting* nor strawberries ripening.

27 Began to cut hay.

29 Dish of peas at table.

AUGUST

1781 **3** Hay put up.

11 Harvest begun in some places; a few small patches of bear cut at Disblair.

17 Harvest begun pretty generally.

1782 **30** After a cold and tempestuous month the leaves of some of the ash and plane trees were *quite withered*. They had been fully out for only two months.

1783 **5** Hay put up.

13 Bear cut everywhere.

20 At Rayne and other places large stacks of bear. General harvest all round there earlier than at Disblair.

28 Bear cut at Disblair.

1784 **5** Hay in the sow.

27 Some bear cut, but oats in general very green. Some early apples ripe.

30 Lint pulled - fine crop.

1785 **27** Some bear cut in different places.

1786 **20** Mid-August wet. Plenty of fruit on geans, but burst with rain. Plenty of gooseberries and small fruit. Apples plentiful, but small. Few pears.

29 Some bear cut; a good deal more would be if weather dry.

30 and 31 Some damage to bear crop by violent wind.

1787 **11** Hay in stack or sow.

13 Improvement in crop since beginning of month. Now all shot and bear filling well.

24 Very little of the bear had begun to change colour.

1788 **3** Hay put in a sow.

8 Potatoes at table.

21 Bear changing colour everywhere. Cutting in early districts.

22 A great deal of small fruit. Obliged to sell some gooseberries at 10 pence the peck.

23 Began cutting bear at Disblair.

24 Everyone cutting bear - ripening fast.

1789 **2** Swarm of bees - fourth from four stools.

15 Got hay put in sow.

28 Harvest coming on in several places. Some bear cut down.

28 to 3 September Rivers and burns in spate. Harm to haugh corn.

1790 **23 and 24** After a cold month with a great deal of rain, a storm of wind led to fears that the crop would be hurt by the roots being loosened.

31 Cutting bear by this date.

1791 **22** Some bear cut about Aberdeen.

31 A good deal of bear and peas cut down in many places.

1792 **17** Bear beginning to change colour.

28 Frost caused leaves of plane and birch trees to turn brown and fall off.

1793 The only entries were about the weather which was very wet. Hot and thundery at the beginning and cold later.

1794 **1** Some bear cut down near Disblair.

25 A great deal of bear cut down round Disblair. Crop coming *fast forward*. **27** Harvest going briskly.

1795 **11** Two months since peas were in full flower and not one to full size yet. Apples and pears never swelling, and apples dropping off. Gooseberries green as ever.

12 First hot day that year.

SEPTEMBER

1781 Wet month. River Don over the haughs, in some places four times. Bear crop damaged.

11 Field of oats at Disblair cut.

13 A good deal of the crop in. Most of the apples from the standard trees picked.

1782 **6** A few stooks of bear seen at Hatton of Fintry. Oats all quite green.

14 Began to cut a small park of bear. Potatoes pretty large.

1783 **1** Cut most of English oats

4 and 5 Remainder of bear and English oats cut.

6 Took in some bear.

11 Bear, English oats and white peas all gathered in.

16 Everybody cutting and carting.

18 Took in oats cut on **15th.**

25 Bear and English oats all in almost everywhere – fine crop of both. Own country oats not cut as not yet ripe and flattened by rain and wind.

1784 **12** Some bear cut in most places and some early English oats, but no continuous harvesting anywhere. Oat crop in general still very green in spite of recent good spell of weather.

15 Bear at Disblair cut.

19 General harvest now - crop came on unexpectedly fast.

30 All bear and peas at Disblair taken in.

1785 **8** Began cutting bear at Disblair, but stopped by rain.

12 Remainder of bear cut.

17 Some oats cut at Disblair.

30 Got in some bear.

1786   16 Cut down field peas.

18 Bear taken in and early oats. Little of *our own kind of oats* cut down.

22 Began to cut some oats, but most of it not ready.

1787   5 Good deal of bear cut near Aberdeen and where sown early.

10 Everybody cutting bear.

25 The crop thought good everywhere, if got safely in.

27 Began to cut corn.

1788   9 Everyone cutting bear and early oats. Early apples and pears ripe and picked.

20 A great deal cut down and a good deal taken in.

27 *Done with our harvest.*

1789   10 Bear at Disblair cut.

14 Everyone cutting bear.

16 Got in the bear.

19 **and 20** River Don over the haughs - a good deal of bear carried off.

24 Corn still green.

1790   5 Bear ready for cutting for most part round Disblair, but nothing done on account of rain. Great deal of bear and early oats cut around Aberdeen.

8 Cut down the bear that was ripe.

13 Put the cut bear in a stack.

19 Crop all laid after heavy rain. Trees all yellow as at the end of October, except the ash.

23 Last of bear cut at Disblair.

24 Cut a little ripe oats.

29 Cut oats.

30 Got in first cut bear.

1791   10 Many small parcels of bear cut down.

15 Much bear cut down and a good deal taken in.

1792   7 After three or four dry days, *cut down our Bear*.

15 Snow in morning. Cold day - frost at night. Tops of potatoes and French beans taken off.

18 Oats cut in different places. Great deal of crop laid flat to the ground.

28 Began to cut corn. Great deal cut down everywhere though not dry nor *in good case*.

1793   18 Everyone cutting bear.

19 Began to cut bear at Disblair and got it finished that evening.

25 Began to cut oats.

1794   **6** Good harvest weather. Many stacks of bear and oats in the yards.

      8 Harvest finished.

      13 *Got our little crop all into the yard.*

      23 Corn shaken by strong winds.

      24 Everyone busy at the hook.

OCTOBER

1781   **1** Most of the corn in.

1782   **6** Bear into the yard, but not very dry. Peas cut down.

      13 Much of the oat crop still green. Bear not all cut and very little gathered in in most places.

      20 Snow most of the day. Oats hardly changed colour. Very little of the crop in general cut down and gathered in throughout the whole country.

      24 After three dry days everybody cutting down and taking in as quickly as possible – ripe or green.

1783   **4** Cut more oats. Much still unripe.

      7 Took in what was cut on **4th**.

      9 Last of corn cut at Disblair. Harvest finished in early places.

1784   **12** Oats cut, except one piece of English oats which was quite green. In early dry ground harvest finished. Not half done in most places.

      31 Snow came during the month. What had been cut was not keeping and everybody afraid to take in what was cut or cut what was not ripe.

1785   **1** Took in the rest of bear.

      3 Cut down the last of the corn and carted a good deal of the first cut.

      10 Got in remainder of oats.

1786   **3** Cut down more oats. None in yet.

      9 Put up small stack of first cut oats.

      14 Great deal of crop to cut and a great deal in stooks which were wet through.

      16 Last of corn cut and got in small stack.

      17 Took in a little more corn.

      28 Got in the last of the corn.

1787   **2** Most of bear cut and a great deal in, but little oats except in early places. Potatoes lifted at Disblair. Good crop everywhere.

      12 Oats flattened by storm of wind and rain.

      17 Last of oats cut. Everybody cutting, but none can be taken in.

      24 Got in a good deal. Everybody leading.

31 Great deal of corn in stack and much to cut down. What was in the yard was not keeping.

1788   **3** Frost. Very little round Disblair to cut or cart.

       13 Fine crop of potatoes. Turnips looking fine.

1789   **1 to 12** So much rain that the stooks were wet through and what was on the ground was beaten down and some of it starting to grow. Very little oats got in.

       13 Cut some corn.

       16 and 17 Rest of Disblair oats cut.

       18 Most of cut corn growing green in the stooks.

       29 A great deal of the crop cut and taken in. All thatched at Disblair.

1790   **5** Most of the bear in - a great deal cut and taken in around Disblair.

       6 All the oats cut.

       7 Bear all in and thatched.

       8 Got in some oats.

       10 Got in more oats.

       14 All the crop in and stacks thatched.

       19 All the crop around Disblair in.

1791   **8** *Got our little harvest finished.*

       13 Got in most of our corn.

       26 A great deal to cut down and in stooks. Pretty fair to the end of the month and all round Disblair mostly got in.

1792   **2** Everyone cutting.

       6 A great deal cut and taken in. Most of Disblair's in the yard and little to cut.

       13 Cut the last of the crop.

       14 Much to cut down and take in in many places and what was in stacks was heating.

       16 Most of Disblair corn cut, but much to cut down and take in over all that part of Aberdeenshire.

       25 *Came to Aberdeen.*

1793   **1** Everyone leading and cutting.

       3 Cut down oats that were ready, but *much hereabouts still very green.*

       7 Got in all oats cut.

       14 A good deal still to cut.

Very little frost that month. All flowers were in *as great Blow as any time in Summer. Few Trees in Autumn Colours.*

       19 Last of Disblair corn cut. Still a great deal to cut down and take in elsewhere.

24 *Came to Aberdeen.*

1794   4 Harvest finished everywhere. Crop thin and short.

23 Great many pears and apples, but not keeping any time.

30 *Came to Aberdeen.*

NOVEMBER

1782 19 Oats cut and some taken in.

1783 15 Severe frost. *Came to Aberdeen.*

23 Cattle still getting food all day in the fields and ploughing almost finished.

1784   1 Last of oats at Disblair cut.

12 Last of Disblair oats taken in.

15 Harvest finished in that area and in most districts, except in very late places.

22 Intense frost stopped all ploughing.

1785   3 Crop not all cut down in many places and much to cart.

1786 17 All crop in except in very late places.

1787 14 (Wet month so far) A great deal still to cut and take in.

1788 17 **to** 25 Mild, fine weather. Grass and everything as green as in summer.

1789   3 Great deal of the crop still in the stook, and to cut down North and South of Disblair. *Much will be lost. Came to Aberdeen.* All round there great fields to cut and much to stook.

5 **and** 6 Rain. Much of the crop brought down by the rivers.

9 **to** 16 Still a great deal of rain. Much of the crop rotting everywhere - S. Scotland and N. England no better.

27 *the Drum going for Huiks to Cut doun Corn within Some Mills of Abd. The Crop not all got in Yet South nor North.*

1790   6 Severe flooding on River Don brought down a great deal of corn that was in *hutts* on the haughs and one stack of oats.

1791   3 *Came to Aberdeen.*

1792   8 Crop now all got in in almost every part of Aberdeenshire.

1793 13 The crop now got in everywhere, except in very late places.

1794 Stormy, with severe gales towards the end of the month.

DECEMBER

1782   8 Some hill farms above Monymusk still not even cut. Little ploughing done.

1783 Fine, open weather for first three weeks followed by strong winds and heavy falls of snow.

1784 Frost and snow for most of the month.

DISBLAIR HOUSE, ABERDEENSHIRE – 1781 TO 1795

	Seedtime				Haymaking		Harvest	
	Oats		Bear					
1781	–	15 Mar.	–	17 May	18 July	3 Aug.	11 Aug.	1 Oct.
1782	8 Apr.	24 Apr.	21 May	28 May	–	–	14 Sept.	4 Dec.
1783	18 Mar.	9 Apr.	12 Apr.	9 May	17 July	5 Aug.	29 July	9 Oct.
1784	19 Apr.	28 Apr.	6 May	22 May	9 July	5 Aug.	27 Aug.	15 Nov.
1785	11 Apr.	17 Apr.	24 Apr.	21 May	12 July	–	8 Sept.	10 Oct.
1786	6 Apr.	–	26 Apr.	20 May	c. 10 July	22 July	29 Aug.	28 Oct.
1787	17 Mar.	12 Apr.	7 May	16 May	3 July	23 July	10 Sept.	1 Dec.
1788	14 Apr.	27 Apr.	29 Apr.	22 May	4 July	3 Aug.	23 Aug.	27 Sept.
1789	13 Apr.	22 Apr.	2 May	–	4 July	15 Aug.	28 Aug.	29 Oct.
1790	1 Mar	12 Apr.	21 Apr.	13 May	9 July	–	8 Sept.	14 Oct.
1791	14 Mar	28 Apr.	–	–	11 July	18 July	10 Sept	13 Oct.
1792	22 Mar.	6 Apr.	–	–	16 July	24 July	7 Sept.	16 Oct.
1793	–	2 May	c. 5 May	11 May	18 July	–	19 Sept	13 Nov.
1794	16 Mar	26 Mar.	–	3 May	–	–	25 Aug.	13 Sept.
1795	–	–	–	–	27 July	28 Aug.	–	–

Table 3 – Dates for the beginning and ending of sowing, haymaking and harvest 1781 to 1975

1785 Changeable weather with a good deal of snow towards the end of the month.
1786 Unsettled weather with more rain than snow.
1787　1 Crop all in.
Frost followed by heavy rain and flooding. Snow towards end of month.
1788 First week mild followed by frost and a good deal of snow.
1789　**11** Ploughing going on briskly. Rain and snow during remainder of month.
1790　**17** Ploughing far advanced. Corn and fodder up the country very cheap. Weather changeable.
1791 Hard frost followed by heavy snow.
19 More snow. *Traveling Very Bad.*
1792　**9** *that night the wind Rose to such a hight that few People remembers to have heard anything like it.* Generally unsettled.
1793 Rain, cold at times, but no snow.
1794 Strong winds followed by inconstant weather with no snow until the end of the month.

	SEEDTIME	HARVEST	TOTAL (SEED TO YARD)
1781	–	7	–
1782	7	12	34
1783	8	10	29
1784	5	12	31
1785	6	5	26
1786	7	9	29
1787	9	12	37
1788	5	5	24
1789	–	8	28
1790	11	5	31
1791	–	5	30
1792	–	6	29
1793	–	8	–
1794	7	3	26

Table 4 – Length of time in weeks for seedtime, harvest and the whole period of activity on the farm from the sowing of the first seeds to the completion of the stacks in the yard.

OF THE

DIARY

OF JANET BURNET

1758 TO 1795

Kemnay 1758

21 May Cut Spinage that was sown that Year & had Peas in full Blosom – The 18 June we had a full Ashet of Peas & some Cherries and Strawberries.

In the Year 1760 we had a dish of Green Peas the 11th of June.

1762 the 2d April I walked Round a part of Kemnay Parks on the Snow – it being as high as the Dyck and hard & firm to walk on & much Snow over all the Ground. Yet this year We Cut Spinag sown that Year the 17th May & had a Dish of Peas sown that Year the 16 june & had also Artichocks & some Rip Strawberries.

1765 Exceding hot weather End of July to the 10 August after that Cold as winter with high winds & stormy sea.
Oor Green Peas & Artichocks was only at table the 3 Jully & Tasted some Strawberries & Cherries in the Garden.

1766

Green Peas the 8 Jully & a Dish of Strawberries & Cherries the 12 of Jully.

1768

We had Green Peas the 18 of june & Cherries & Strawberries several times at table before the 29.

in 1771 we Cut a Mellon which wighted 2½ pound it measurd 17 Inches Round.

1766

Janr   Frosty weather till the 17 from that to the 26th fair – from that to the End of the Month Rain & Frost by turns.
Febr   frost & Snow till the 15th Frost till the 20th Snow frost & fair by turns till the End

March   Rain & wind to the 4th fair all day & frost at Night till the 17th Rain till the 22d Snow to the End

April   Snow laying on the Ground With fair weather till the 7th fair weather & frost till the 18th Snow from this to the 26 fair to the End

May   first two days fair – from that Rain every Day till the 13 then two days Snow - Rain & wind & often frost till the End

June   Rain the first 3 Days fair till the 9 then one night frost - Rain till the 22th then fair to the End

Jully   4 days fair 4 Days Rain 5 Days fair 2 Days Rain 4 Days fair 4 Days Rain 3 Days fair 2 days Loud wind 2 Days fair.

August mostly fair till 6th – then one Nights frost – then fair till the 14th one Day Rain & wind then fair till the 24 – frost again & Rain & fair till the End

Septr   One Night Frost – pretty fair weather till the 10th Rain & wind & sometimes frost at night till the 20th fair to the End

Octr   Fair till the 8th frosty fair weather till the 22d Rain - wind & frost by turns till the End

Novr   fair till the 15 except two Days Rain & wind – Rain & wind other 2 Days then fair to the 26 – One Day Snow & Rain frost to the End

Decr   Mostly fair only two or three days Rain & wind One Day Snow & 3 hard Frost

This Year 80 Days Rain 35 Days Snow on the Ground & 17 Days wind

1767

Janr   Frost & Snow the whole month

Febr   Snow on the Ground till the 9th Frost till the 19th Wind & Rain - & frost in the Night till the End

March   fair with frost at Night till the 12th Frost & Snow till the 22d Rain till the 29th Rain & wind the last 2 Days

April   Pritty fair weather till 14th Frost till the 18th Rain & Snow till the 24 Fair till the End

May   wind & Snow till the 4th fair till the 18h Rain & fair by turns & often Frost at Night till the End

June   Rain & fair by turns & frost at Night for most part till the 12th fair to the End Except some showrs the 26 & 27 Loud winds

Jully   first two Days Loud winds Rain every Day till the last Day which was a Loud Wind

August Rain 9 Days at diffrend times the rest fair weather

Sept   Fair with Showrs now & then till the 28 one Day Wind & Rain then fair till the End –

October 8 Days fair all this Month the rest Rain & three Days Loud Wind & Rain – & fresh at Night

Novr Rain & fair by turns to the End only one Day Windy –

Decr Snow two first Days then Rain fair & frost by turns till 25 – Frost & Snow till the End –

In this Year 115 Days of rain 60 Days Snow on the Ground 24 Days of Wind –

1768

Jan^r   Frost & Snow till the 12th fair & frost till the 20th Snow & frost till the 24th Rain & fair till the End

Feb^r   frost & fair till the 8th Snow on the Ground till the 23^d Rain & fair by turns till the End

March Snow till the 6th Frost & fair till the 13 Snow till the 17th Rain & fair with frost at Night till the End

May   first two Days frost – from that to the End fair Except 2 Days of Rain & one of Wind

June   fair till the 10th Rain with two Days Wind till the 23^d fair till the End

Jully   Rain Every Day Excepting six day till the End

August Rain till the 6th then two Days Loud wind & fair till the End

Sept^r   Rain & fair by turns till the 6th fair till the 15th Rain till the 26th – fair & frost at Night till the End – The greatest overflowing of the River Don Ever known

Octr Rain & fair by turns & frost at Night the whol Month

Novr Rain & wind frost & fair with some snow by turns the whol Month

Decr frost till the 17th Rain & fair by turns & frost at Night till the 28 then Snow & frost till the End

In this Year 103 days Rain 37 days Snow on the Ground   Loud winds 13 days

    Kemnay 1772 the Storm Came on the 6 Jan^r, it Lay till the 12 March there was no Blowing & hardly a Day of thaw till the 27 Feb^r when we measurd the Snow it was 20 Inches over the whol Ground – this Storm did not go off so as any Plough Could enter the Ground till the 12 of March when the snow Continowd to Melt the hight of the Day, but Frost at Night & some new falls of snow till the End

of April – never any kindly Thaw but the work went on & Kemnays Bear seed was done the 7th May
the 14 had a Large Cukember

1773 Jan^r 18 the Mercury fell so Low allmost out of sight the Index would not point it – a pritty Loud wind that Day the 19 Calm – 20 from 8 to 10 o clock a Voilent wind Blowd Down four hundr Trees at Kemnay

The Storm begun Christmas Day but did not snow much till the first of Jan^r <u>1774</u> when the Snow was very deep, & Lay till the 4 of Feb^r. every week more Snow – then we had two days Thaw [this Snow Measurd 14 Inches over all] & then more Snow. It begun to Thaw again the 12th & Continowd to go off Gently without Rain, but we had frost at Night – After this Storm went off, we had not three weeks of dry, or fair, weather, till Hervest which was begun the 9 Sept. We had then 3 weeks of fine dry weather, in which time Every Body was so diligent that most of the Crop was got doun & taken in. A few days after, which was the 4th of Novr we had Snow but soon went off & Rain came on again & seldom keept off one day till Christmas

Jan^r <u>1775</u> fine weather all that Month. Feb^r was so fine Dry, Blowing Weather that Kemnay begun his <u>Oat Seed the first of March</u>. no Snow or frost, but for a day or so all the winter. the whol Month of March was Blowing Weather & many Days of wind so Loud that we Could not go out to walk – Yet the Earth being so Sockd & Beat with the Long Continowance of Rain we had before that there was no Dust Raisd with the Harrows the Oat Seed was <u>finished the 25 March</u> – The 26 Came on a Storm of Snow & hard frost & we <u>filld oor Ice House</u> which Could no be don all winter.
was continowd but Eight Days & the Winds begun again, and continowd Blowing weather till the Midle of April.

1775

then we had a fortnight of as warm weather as if June. the <u>Bear seed was finished the 3d of May</u> – the <u>Honysuckle fully Blown</u> - 9 of May no Rain all this time, but a few Showrs. Our Peats was Cast the 6 of May. Cold Loud winds again but no Rain – 9 of June still no Rain – the 10th <u>a Bee Hive</u> swarmed & that Day <u>had a Dish Green Peas</u> - Dry hot Weather which Continowd throu the whol Summer, & hardly any Rain – the Crop in General thin & short – the 4th <u>of August</u> we begun Hervest & had all in the Yard the 9 of Sept^r , & all the Rucks Thatchd - the weather so long dry that We was Obliged to take oor Hors & Cattle to the River of Don to watter them – but the Spring that Serves the House Run as brisk & full as Ever –

the weather Continowd open & fine till the 7th Janr 1776 that day we had some snow, which incresd & Continowd falling three days & quit Calm weather We measurd the snow & Computed 14 Inches over all. It Continowd quit Calm, & the frost Moderate till the 19th when We had four Days Drift & Blowing weather & Record two Inches more snow The snow Continowd to lay & Calm weather & not sever Frost till the 1th of Febr when it begun to Thaw & the 8th the Plugh was going, but always frost at Night. this made the Wreath still lay the 15th no wheel Carrige Could go from Kemnay to Aberdeen nor any Place Round. This Storm was more sever in England, & was deeper South & North. It Came on the same way, & at the same time Every way – & at London & Nairn The Thaw begun the very same day it did at Kemnay.

the 2d of March another great fall of snow but it only Lay three days, & after that Mild fine Weather & no Rain all this Month. The Oat Seed was don 2d April. This Year the Trees most Remarkably full Flowrishd & every shrub Beautifull the Firs & every Tree Loaded with Seed. May Cold, Frost & winds destroyed most of the Plumbs, & Pears, & kept Back the Grass. A Cukember Cut the 26 May

after this fine Seasonable weather, the whole Summer, & a fine Crop Especialy of Bear the Greatest Quantity of Fruit Every way in this Country – and also in England – We Could not Use the One half of oor Aples & what was sold give but 10 pence for two slicks of the Corn Peck.

The Hearvest begun 2d Septr & was finishd & all in the Yard the 1th of Octr the 4th there was a severe Frost – the Crop was in General good this Year only a Nights Frost that happend the begining of Septr, & took off all the Tops of the Petatos , was thought to have hurt the Crop in late Low Grounds – the Pears this Year did not keep any time was all soon for Eating, sweld & Crackd as if Bursting which we imputed to that Frost & non of the Fruit was so high flavourd as usual —– The Weather was fine as possible & little Frost & only one Windy Day till the 16th Decr when we had a showr of snow from this to the

4th Janr 1777 we had Frost fresh & showrs of snow - then we had heavy snow & Blowing for three days which made the Roads impassable in some parts. The Post Could not go from Stonhive to

Ab^d. & the Meal was brought in by three Men, as no Hor^s Could go.

1777

this Continowd till the 12th when we had a Brisk Thaw – This Storm not deep only Computed 4 or 5 Inches – We filld oor Ice House with Ice from the Bridg of Don the 13th – The 16 Frost & more Snow. 22^d It Thawd very Brisk, & in two Days the snow mostly gon & the Plughs going – fine warm days as if Summer till the 8th of March that day Cold & some snow, the 9 & 10th more snow & Frost at Night all this Month Work going slowly on the first Eight days of April dry sunny days but still some Frost at Night - The 9 the Oat Seed finishd – after this dry hard Cold Air & Frost Every Night the 20th the Frost so strong that the Watter in the Wilderness was quit Frose over still strong frost & showrs of snow all this Month – The 30th going to Seaton, We Could not see out at the Windows of the Chais for snow

May the first Rain Cold all this Month – and all the Month of June Cold – Sometimes Rain, & sometimes frost so as we could not want a Fire throw out the whole day – no appearance of Fruit of any kind this year, and no seed on the Firs, or on any Tree – Jully warm days to the 10th. The Bees swarmed & few Strawberries ready – after this Cold & Rain Every day the last three Days of this Month it Rained Night & Day without an Hours intermition –

12 August only one Day without Rain since this Month begun the Crop Mended greatly & looking well & Rich as can be, but the Hay in much danger of being spoild – till the End of this Month much dryer the Hay here all got in safe – There was two days of Exceding Loud Wind which hurt the Bear when it was well filld or near Rip –

Septr fine dry warm weather the 18th we begun Hearvest but there was Cutting Down Round us a Week befor that It Continowd fair fine Weather till the 27th when the Rain begun & from this till the 7th Octr we had only one smal field Cut Doun – & one smal stack of Bear got in – from this to the 17th very little work don Every Day Rain & no Wind nobody Could remember to have seen so much of the Crop Cut doun & all on the Ground at one time – the 18 dry & fine & a good deal of Bear & Corn taken in this fine dry weather Continowd till the 23^d when oor shearing was finishd & the 25 all got in Some of these days was sever frost & 27th a fall of snow This soon went off, & all Novr fine dry weather, now & then frost –

Decr inconstant Weather Rain – then some snow & hard frost – then Rain Again – till the 25 a little fall of snow & hard frost which Continowd & fine pleasent weather till the 16 Jan^r 1778

then it went off & Mild weather with Rain till the 25th. then
snow again which lay a few days & then Rain this unconstant weather
Continowd all Feb^r, in the End of that Month We <u>filled oor Ice House
with snow</u> – and from that to the 13 March had strong Frost & some
snow & that day filld <u>oor other Ice</u> House at the top of the Hill with
Ice from the Watter of <u>Don</u> – 22 March Rain & Snow & little work
got done – from this to <u>the Second of</u> April fine dry weather & the
Oat seed finishd that day – fine warm weather as in summer till the
13th of April when there came on snow & frost as sever as had been
all winter –

1778 April

The 16 John Brownie shot a Young Dear of 2 Year Old in the
Park of Lochshangie & after that a Young Doe in that Park – from
the Midle to the End of April Every day snow & several mornings the
Trees Coverd as in the Depth of Winter the 23 & 24 the Ground quit
hard with frost at 11 o clok forenoon but the Bear seed finishd –

the 30th May warm Weather but very Rainy the whole Month –
hardly three or four days dry at once the whole Month – but no frost
& a fine apearence of Grass & the Crop looking well except in Low
Grounds – which seem hurt with the Rains – June the 10th the same
weather still Continows – a great deal of Flowrish but Late. The 22^d
June the Rain still Continowd & but a few fair days – Cold with it &
some Thunder & great Showrs of Hail – from the 23^d which day we
begun to slate or new Roof a part of the House, there was dry hot
burning weather to the 5 of Jully – not one drop of Rain – 20th still
the same weather not a showr but one since the 23^d of June – August
14th Eat New Bear Meal – the 26 fine warm weather & little Rain all
this Month – a good deal Cut doun all round us & a good Many Bear
Stacks in the <u>Tennents</u> Yards

the 2^d Septr We begun Hervast the 6 nothing worth while done
Rain Every day – from the 6th to the 26 no Rain to hinder the work,
but the weather most Changable from Excesive hot to Excesive Cold
& this two or three times from the begining of this Month to the 26th
which day oor Hearvest was done & all in the Yard the 29th -

from this to the 12 Novr very few days without Rain some days a
Whit frost & Rain again – that day the Hills all Coverd with snow,
a sever frost & very Cold but the Next day Rain again, & the River
Don Rose very high – the 15 and 16 Loud Winds with Rain, & a
deal of Lightning in the Night time the 17 a great deal of Thunder
& Lightning & all that day was heard in many Places a Noise under

Ground or like a Machin driving at a great distance & what the Common Country People Calls Yerd Din.

from this to the 22 very fine days - but from this to the 13th Decr few days without Rain but Mild & warm not like winter Weather, tho some Mornings a Whit forst – but warm days – the Mavis singing as in summer two at a time from this to the 30 still the same Mild weather. Some few showrs of snow, which did not lay a moment - on the 31th the last day of the Year there arose such a Voilent wind with Drift along with it that a Man lost his Life going from this to Oldrain, & was found some days after in a place off the Road Calld Bograxe. the Blowing & Snow Continowd

the first day of the New Year 1779 but no depth of Snow – & from the 1th to the 17th we had Hard frost & fine sunny days. The most delightfull walking – The 18 we filld oor Low Ice House from the Watter in the Wilderness - the 20th we had a Thaw – The 24 fine Mild fresh weather, & the Mavis singing strongly – 26 a little snow, hard frost & fine Clear sunny days, till the 30th when it Came fresh & foggy weather for some days -

1779

from this to the 26th Feb^r we had no Rain nor Snow, but fine warm Mild Clear Weather. Sometimes a little windy, but no ways disagreeable any Body might have Sown there Grownd, if they pleasd, after the first week of Feb^r – all the Flowrs in the Parler Blown as if the End of April – The Cherrie Plumb in Flowrish fully Blown – the 27 Feb^r begun Oat seed – which might have been don for dry grownd, & weather, but thought too soon -

from this to the 3d March Loud Winds, & this succeded by foggy weather for some days, but still warm – The 7th a little frost in the Night, the only touch of Frost for a Month past – The Grass Parks quit Green, & so long that all the young Cattle put on them & out all Night in the feald – Rose Bushes – Goosberrie Bushes &c &c all Green, & some Trees of Hathorn – A Feald of Turnip all in flowr & Yellow all over

13th March Oat Seed finishd & not a showr since it begun but fine mild weather – only two Nights we had a little frost the 14th some showrs of Rain 16 th & 17 th Frost in the Night but Exceding Warm Days like june or Jully – A standard Cherry Plumb all whit over with Flowrish – other Plumbs the Flowrish Blown, & a good deal of Pear Flowrish opend – Still warm & Mild weather till the 22d when we had three days Loud Wind from the South – but still no Rain – 24 the Plain Tree out & the Leaf expand – Pears & Plumb Trees all whit over – 27

44

& 28 Frost in the Night, still no Rain, & all the Ditches almost dry – The Turnip Park like a feald of skelly & a vast hight the 30th the Cherries & Damsons in full Blown Flowrish, & a good deal of Aple Flowrish & some Strawberries Flowrish still Frost in the Night time, & hot Burning Sune all day

4th April still the same weather, Frost at Night, & hot sunshine all day, & no Rain, not a Showr – this being the first Sunday of April New Still – the Birch Leaf penny Broad, & many other Trees fare advanced, The Gin Trees here – some of them in Flowrish – but the Old Gin Trees at Castle Fraser ready to shuk off there Flowrish with the first Puff of wind – the Peas in Blossom – the 7th April & still the same weather –

from the 7th to the 13th exceding Loud winds, with flying showrs – & Frost at Night, & very Cold – Pears set & as big as Peas – & Cherry Plumbs Larger – the 17th Bear seed begun – the 26th still no Rain – Cold Loud wind & some Nights a little Frost. Cherries well advanced , Strawberries in full Blossom and a good deal seed on the firs, & all the Trees – 29th the same weather only the Frost stronger, & some snow on the Hills, & some showrs of Hail – the same weather Continowd till the 30th when we had a hearty Rain all that afternoon – the Bear Seed Finished – after the Rain Frost at Night –

May 1th we had Wind & Hail & the 2d day very Cold – befor the Morning of the 3d there was a heavey fall of Snow by Measuring we Computed 3½ Inches over all – that Morning the Ice House at the Top of the Hill was filld with Snow by the Gardner – The Trees was all Loaded with it, as if in the depth of Winter, & it was very Odd looking to see the Honeysuckle & Aple Flowrish Reid, & the Scarlet Cons of the Firs, all Pepping throw the whit Snow –

1779

the snow was all gon Eir Night but we had Frost & Rain by turns till the 8th – That day we had Sallad of this years sowing – Coukember & Young Turnip – the 9 a good heavey Rain – from that to the 15, dry Cold wind with frost - that & the 16 Rain & warm

from this to the 26 pritty warm sunny days, And some flying showrs, but frost at Night for the most part – that Day we had a Dish of Turnips.

from the Midle of April to the Midle of May, Everything seemed to go Back, or stand still not a Leafe Broder that withstood the frost – Many of the Trees but Especialy the Fruit Trees quit weatherd, & dryd like snuff – all the Flowrish gon off, & most of the set Fruit – the Grass Much hurt – 29 hot Sunny Days but no Rain, & often frost at Night – Some Pods of Green Peas that was in Blosom the 4 April quit full – all the rest of them taken of by the Frost & Snow – the Peas sown in March in full Blosom & will be the first

---

The 2^d June sitting by the watter in the Wilderness we seed a Piller of Watter Rise as high as the talest Tree & fall doun again, after which it Rolld along for a Considerable space in large Rolls, as if a Vast Cask had been under the Watter, & out of those Rolls, sprung up smal strins of Watter, Rising pritty high, as out of the strup of a Razer – The Noise it Made was such as a fire work of Powder makes when first set off, but much Louder – The Day was Clear, fine sune shine & not <u>a Breath of Wind</u> – : Cabage at Table – the Weather the same – hot sune, & frost at Night offten & no Rain till the 10th we had some smal showrs & much appearnce of Rain, the Air thick & foggy –

the 11th some good heavey showrs here & in many diffrent Places, but no Thunder – the 14 a scap swarmed – 15 a Dish of Cherries. from the 11th hot Dry weather till the 16,

---

that Day going to Abd seed a Pillar of Dust Rise in the Road before us, a littl – which seemd Round & sollid as high as a House & from that Mounted up in smok, as high as the Eye Could see it. When we Came up to the place we could see no mark it had made in <u>the Road -:</u>

The 19 Cold as Winter with showrs of Rain & Snow & Hail 22 a Dish Green Peas – Opened oor Ice House that was filld in Jan^r, & found it quit full of Ice – had Strawberries for oor Ice Cream.

The 24 a hard frost in the Night – no Rain. 31 still dry Hot Weather, & only one little skiff of a showr since the 22^d –

Jully 2^d some showrs of Rain from that to the 9th the Hottest weather any one remembers. that Day ther was a heavey Rain for some Hours, & a great deal of Thunder, and Lightning, by which two Men & two Horses was Killd, some Mills from Abd on the Banchry Road – from this to the 16th Excesive Hot Weather, not like oor Climat. the 19 we was at Gordon Castle where they had Plumbs Rip & there Earliest Apricoes don & a second kind Ready –

1779

This Hot weather Continowd till the 20th when we had some Rain & wind most of that Day, but not heave Rain, nor Cold – We opened oor Ice House that we filld the 3^d of May & found the Snow much in the same state as when put in, but it froze the Cream very well – from this to the 26 warm Weather & some little showrs, now & then.

that Day from 11 o clock to 2 o clock forenoon We had the Most tremindeous Storm of Thunder & Lightning Ever Rememberd here accompanyd with Large Hail & heavy Rain. At Kintor, the Lightning Came doun a Vent of three Chimneys & struck a Maid on the Leg & a Dog Killd, but she only fealt it numbd for soome Hours – at Clunie & Monymusk several people fealt the same. We heard of no more harm don -

from this to the 1ᵗʰ Augst We had Rain Every day – that Night a great frost that speckled all the Peas, then a great deal of Rain – to the 4ᵗʰ Every day Rain from that to the 13ᵗʰ fine Dry pleasent weather but still exceding warm Hervest begun that day but only the Men servants at work till the 23 that all hands was set to work & all the Crop quit rip. a Great deal Cut doun Every way, & a good deal in the Yards – still the same Weather Continowd, dry & Vastly warm, hardly any wind. Some nights a great Fogg. 27 still exceding hot weather, & no Rain – Pears & Aples all Rip & falling off –

1ᵗʰ Septʳ still Hot Weather, & no Rain, the 2ᵈ & 3ᵈ some Showrs but nothing to hinder shearing 14 & 15 Loud Wind & Colder – oor hervest Don – all oor stacks Thatchd the 17 – from this to the 25 fine weather

the last 3 days of this Month & the 3 first days of Octʳ fine dry pleasent weather – the same weather Continowd with very Little Rain to the 28ᵗʰ. This day a very high wind – the Ground still so dry that in many parts the Plugh Cannot go -

No Fruit keeping this Year the Nonsuch, & keeping Aples all Roting & Spoild –

from the 25 Octʳ to the 5 Novʳ the same weather still Continowd little Rain & warm. That day a Loud wind. from this to the 9ᵗʰ windy some part of the day. the 10 thick heavey sky & smal Rain. the 11 & 12 Rain & wind the 13 heavey Rain all day, 14 Cold with Snow & Hail the hills Coverd with Snow. the next morning all whit & 15 snowd all day, 16 & 17 more snow, & a great frost 18 still showrs of Snow & Frost – no melting – & Cold wind.

---

this autum we had many Trees as fully Flowrishd as in Spring there Fruit set & on the 14 of this Month Novʳ we pulld some Aples as Large as a smal Golden Pippin befor the Snow Came. the Strawberries was in full Blosom. _____

22 the Snow here mostly gon but deep towards the Hills, the

Frost very great, & fine sunshin. This Continowd till the 25 when we had Snow & Hail & sever Frost 26 & 27 showrs of snow Hail & a kind of Rain alternally & sever Frost along with it so as they were walking our the River Don on the Ice

1779

28 this night a Voilent storm of wind & Rain which Continowd all that day & the River rose very high 29 a fine Day – frost & sunshin a good deal of the snow off the hills & quit gon here

this Continowd till the 2ᵈ Decʳ when at night a Voilent wind arose & Snow with it which Continowd all Night & part of Next day, but the Snow not deep – the 9ᵗʰ showrs of snow the fornoon, at Night the wind very Loud, & Drift which Continowd all Night –

from this to the 9 sever frost & sunny days – from that to the 14ᵗʰ Thaw & Frost by turns – That day a Loud wind with Rain & showrs of snow but all snow on the Hills Sever Frost & fresh by Tourns till the 18 when it Raind all day – 19ᵗʰ thick & drizling Rain, but still the hills Coverd with snow. the 21 snow & sever Frost This snow Lay & the Frost Continowd. [not deep & fine traveling] till the 26 -

from that till the 2ᵈ Janʳ 1780 the same weather – that day we had a Brisk thaw which took away most of the Snow here but still very deep on the Hills the 3ᵈ Frost again which we had Every day & Clear days with Bright Sunshin till the 8ᵗʰ we had a little snow – the 9 a little more snow with Strong Frost – We had no more snow but the Frost Continowd intence & Froze many things in the House amongst others a Large jar of Duble Distilld Pepermint Watter was in the Garret but not near a Window – this Continowd till the 16 when it Came Rain & Raind havelie all that Day [oor Low Ice House was filld with Ice from the watter in the Garden the 15]

the 17 frost & some showrs of snow from this to the 23 sever frost & some showrs of snow Every day, (the other Ice House filld) but the snow not 2 Inches deep & fine walking. from the 23 to the 28 sever Frost that day & at night a good deal more snow 29 a Brisk Thaw all day 30 Frost again which Continowd & no snow till the 5ᵗʰ Febʳ when we had a smal skiff of snow here but lookt as if a great deal amongst the Hills. 7 a Cold wind & like to be Thaw [Hors & Carts passing the River Don for some weeks past]

the 8 it Thawd & then frost again - the frost Continowd till the 14 when it Came fresh & Continowd so till 17 then a sever frost again the River Brok with this Thaw, & most of the snow gon the 18ᵗʰ it

Thawd the 19 a Loud wind with snow which Continowd till the 24 the snow was deeper then it had been any time all this winter & a great Frost. The 24 it Came fresh & a Brisk Thaw this Continowd till the 26 when we had another fall of Snow, & hard frost. 27 fresh again, 28 fresh with a Loud wind & all the snow gon Except on the hills – the Plughing begun –

March 1th fresh & Blowing weather which Continowd & the wind some days exceding Loud till the 9th when we had snow & a sever Frost but the 10 fresh again & Loud wind 14 the same weather & the Oat Seed begun – 16 still Loud winds & some showrs of snow but no frost – The 18 a dunright Hurican of wind the whol day & night all the rest of this Month Continowd dry & Loud winds – the Oat Seed don the 29.

1780

April 1th a strong frost – the 2d the frost did not Melt Except where the sun shind the whol day – the 3d it snowd heavey Snow the whol day from this to the 12 sever Frost & few days without snow the Cherrie Plumb on the wall in Flowrish, the Pear flowrish pritty far advanced - 16 still the same weather –

24 still frost in the night & Cold showrs of Rain & hail Every day no parks of Grass looking Green nor any Tree but the Larex - the Work going very Slowly on & no Bear sown yet Many Places the Oat Seed not near don –

from this to the first of May the same weather, from the 1th to the 8th fine dry warm weather & the work going on Briskly the Grass & Brir getting up One Plain Tree the Leaf quit Expanded but not one Birk Leaf peny Broad a good deal of Flowrish Blown – the 12th still fine weather & this day the Bear Seed quit finishd

14 & 15 Rain – all the Fruit Trees in hight of Glory full of Blosom & the Grass & every thing made great progress no frost since this Month began - the 19 all the Hills Coverd with Snow - Rain & Hail here & as Cold as winter. 22 still Cold Rainy weather

from this to the 4 June fine dry warm Mild weather only some frost in the night – some nights – the same weather Continowd – the 6th we had Salad & Cukember that night & three following we had such sever Frost that the Ice was on the Pools in the Morning. the Beach & Ash Trees was all weatherd like Snuff & many things Visibly destroyed – the 9 we had a fine warm Rain all the afternoon but soon Cold again, & frost & showrs of hail – from this to the 19th the same weather some days warmer but Rain Every day the 20 we went up to Pananich Lodg – the weather was still very Cold for Eight days, after which we had two days Exceding hot then showrs high winds & often Frost till the 28 Jully -

from that to the 24 August No Rain but one showr & a vilent Frost after it, & as hot as any weather all last summer. The Hervest begun Round Kemnay to be Constant the 20th of August –

We had Plenty of Melons this year the first Cut the End of june and at that time plenty of Cukembers – Peas, Strawberries the 20 of Jully, & Cherries – Vast Plenty of Gins this year – We Opened oor Low Ice House 21 August & had Plenty of Ice -

28 begun Hervest the weather Continowd hot & not a drop of Rain till the 8 Septr we had a wind & Colder Weather the same weather & no Rain till the 15 when that day & the 16 Rain the 17 a great deal of Rain 18 fair & warm from this to the 23 warm Closs weather with frost at night – this day oor Hervest was finishd & the 28 all got in to the Yard. this year a great deal of Fruit – Sold Gins & some Goosberries – & 2 Bolls 1 firlot & 1½ pecks Aples

Disblair May the 1th 1781 the Plain Tree & Hors Chesnut fully out some Leaves quit expanded about 8 Days ago – the Cherrie Trees, Apples & Pears in full Blosom – Every Body around this don with there Oat Seed about the Midle of March this Year – The weather dry but frost at Night – The 2^d a great fall of Rain 3 & 4 more Rain. from this to the 13th Exceding Cold with showrs of hail or Rain & sever Frost Every Night

from the 13th to the 21th some warm days & showrs of Rain but succeded by Cold hard Air, & sever frost at Night – the 22 & 23 the frost in the morning two Inch into the Ground [All the Bear Seed Round this don about the Midle of this Month] 24 Spinage Cutt & Plenty of Radish Strawberries in Flowrish – from this to the End of the Month no Frost but dry Windy weather & exceding hot the Peas in full Blosom the Hathorn Laburnum & Raon Trees

The 1th june some Rain & Thunder – The 2^d Exceding warm & sunshin from this to the 19 Foggy weather & few Days we Could want a Fire. from that to the 29th only one Day a little Rain. all Dry weather mostly windy & not warm. the Hay Crop poor Every way the 30th had a Large Dish Green Peas & a Dish Strawberries & some Cherries Rip – this Day some Rain.

The first of Jully warm but dry & windy – from the first to the 18 frequent Rain & warm which made a great Chang on the Crop, & Grass to the better. this Day begun to Cut oor Hay which was Ripd for Seed – there was a great deal fine seed it was stackd & threshd out the 22 – dry sunny weather & exceding Hot all the rest of this Month only one day some Thunder & a little Rain

The 3 of August the Hay put up from this to the 11 th still the same weather only some days foggy & Closs weather, hardly any watter to be got for the Beasts, but the well for the House keeping up very well. Hervest begun in some Places – some little Yards of Bear Cut here – this night from 9 o clock to 11 a great deal of Thunder & Lightning but little Rain. The 12th a great deal of Thunder with some showrs of Rain. The 13 more Thunder all at a distance & little Rain. The 14 Gloomy Sky & Showrs of Rain. The 15 from Eleven fornoon to 7 night it Raind without intermition as heavy as the greatest Thunder showr I ever seed, but One. 16 & 17 still Rain & many Voilent showrs of Hail & Rain Hervest now begun pritty Genral the 19 very Cold & frost at night 20 the Bear in the Garden Cut doun 23 still very Cold & some showrs of Rain – from this to the 29 Constant Rain.

Saturday Sept 1th a Very Loud wind that shook a great deal of the Corns 2d & 3d pritty dry 4 th a great deal more Rain much of the Bear Crop hurt by the Rains & the River, being over the haughs in some places four times – the 11th oor park of Corn Cut doun (4 days work to seven hooks) from the 4th to the 13th fair & warm with foggs at Night, a good deal of the Crop taken in. Most of oor Aples taken in – that was on the Standards 14th & 15th fair & dry Air, took in the half of the Corn first Cut doun.

1781 Septr

16 Rain most of the Day 17th in the morning got in the rest of Corn from one to four o clock a great deal of Thunder & Lightning much Louder & nearer than any this Year, with most heavey Rain the Burn Came doun with such Voilince as to Come over the Top of some ston Dykes & throw doun others in its way & sweep all befor it – the Top of the Parapet of the Bridg at Old Mill was all that was Visibel. from this to the 23d pritty dry mild weather & a great deal taken in & very Cold – The rest of this month much such weather –

from the 1th of Octr to the 10th very fine Weather – that Night a Voilent storm of wind – the Corn Mostly in every way the begining of this Month – from this to the 18 fine warm suney weather – The 19 & 20 Cold & Blowing this Continowd with some showrs of snow till the 24, then Mild warm days till the 29 then Rain [a fine Crop of Turnip & Petatoes] till the first of Novr that Day a good fall of Snow 2d more snow 3d fresh & the snow mostly gon 4th frost & suney – from this to the End of the Month Loud Wind succeded by Voilent Rain then a day frost & a showr of Snow – Then the Loud Wind, & Rain again –

This weather Continowd till the 15th Janry <u>1782</u> when we had a more sever Frost & some Snow from this to the 20 Frost & showrs of snow & some days fresh. This weather Continowd mostly frost & some snow on the Ground till End of the Month, & some days Blowing & drift, but still little Snow on the Ground.

The first of Febr we had more snow & it Continowd till the 8, when we had a good deep Storm on the Ground. 14 the storm still growing, & strong Frost, the Snow Computed 8 Inches over all. The Storm Continowd till the 22 when It thawd that & next day, with a good deal of Rain, but very Cold. from this to the 28 very little frost Rain & Blowing weather but the Snow in the Hills little melted.

1th March the snow mostly gon in the Low Country but still in the Hills – frost in the Night & Suney Days 4th Cold & Exceding high winds, the above weather by turns Continowd till the 11th when it Snowd, the 12 a great deal of Snow with Blowing Many Cottages & Sheep Coats quit Coverd & all traveling with Carriges made imposible Especialy to the North – the wreathes being so great – from the 12 to the 25 more Snow every day & the Storm no ways decressd as the new Snow makes up all the heat of the Sun Melts the high ways more passable but in many parts of the Country no Communication Can be opend. Many Houses in Abd the Snow never off the Roofs Since this Storm begun, nor the Street Clear of Snow. 26 It begun to Thaw, the Wind came in to the South & we had a good Rain next day, & the weather warmer. This Continowd with Some pritty Loud winds, & some Rain till the

1th April when most of the Snow was gon Except in the Hills & where There was great wreaths of Snow. This Day begun Oat Seed here & Sowd some feald peas – much the same weather with frost at nights till the 8th when we left Abd. We found very little Plughing don round here & hardly any seed sown, the 9 a fine day & work going on Briskly -

1782 April

The 10th a new fall of Snow, all the Ground Coverd & the Trees Loaded with Snow, it Lay all that & next day. 12th Showrs of Snow, but the sun & lenth of the Day melted the Snow – 18 Still bitter Cold & every day since the 12th frost & Showrs of hail or Snow – the work & sowing going very slowly on & many Places no seed put in the grownd – Not the lest mark of Vigetation, all as winter 21th still Cold Blick days but little Rain since the 18th & a great deal sown this last week. all don here Except Low watt grownd but not one Leaf on the Trees, not even on the Goosberrie Bushes – Snow still in the Hills & mostly frost at Night

24 all the Low ground Sown & mostly don herabout, but in many Places little don. Rain this day & Snow in the Hills. 25 Exceding Cold & Showrs of Snow frost at Night 26 bitter Cold & hail 30 Every day heavy showrs of snow & hail & bitter Cold winds – the Peas that was just above Grownd when we came here (8 April) not half an Inch above it yet – not one Goosberrie Bush fully Leaved, nor a Bud on any Tree Expanded, but the Flowrish buds ready to Burst Could they get one warm day.

1th May went to Kemnay nothing there more advanced than here. Still the same weather 5th May still the same – hail & snow every day & sever Frost at Night 11th Yesterday & this day no hail or snow but still Cold, & Frost at Night the fare of Hills still as whit as in the Midle of Storm some Bear sown at Straloch in many Places Oat Seed not don

12 May no Frost last Night & the Air more soft this day Some Blosom opend on the Plumb Cherry & Aple Trees – Some Larch begins to look Green – the Grass beginning to look better & get up a little a Park of Bear Sown here the 11th – the Goosberrie Bushes not fully Leafd yet – a great Number of Feltifers & Several Wood larks seen here this day – 13 a fine warm Rain last Night & this day a little Rain here, but Cold – a great deal of Rain & some Thunder at a great distance. 14 Cold & Windy from this to the 18 a good deal of Rain, but still Cold 19 & 20 Showrs of Snow in the morning, & the near Hills whit for a little – the Distant Hills still unmelted & whit as winter. 21 & 22 dry suney & a good deal of wind but sever Frost at night but the Ground dryd, & the Bear Seed going on – 23d dry & Suney – not a Bud burst on any Forest Tree, but the Larch. 26 the same weather Continowd till this day when we have the Ground all whit with Hail* & a good deal of Loud Thunder – the Plain Tree Buds opend & some few Leaves on the Hathorn little Flowrish on the Fruit Trees got out yet.

*This Hail Lay unmelted & the Ground all whit from 12 oclock fornoon till 8 at Night.

27th & 28 pritty fair & the work going on Bear Seed mostly throw in some places others hardly begun. 29 & 30 most Voilent Rain the Burn here impassable for all the Bridg, for most of a Day – the Rivers all very high & a stop put to all work – 31th some showrs –

1th June dry & some wind but still very Cold – from the first to the 7th the same, only some smal showrs, the 8th thick & foggy the 9 Rain Most of the day – The Plain Elm Birch & Laburnum shown there Leaf but not one Tree in full foilage yet – not one Sprige of Flowrish on the Standard Fruit Trees –

1782

little more Blown on the Pears & Aples on the Wall than there was 28th last month – the Cherry in full Blosom endeed, but nothing Else in the Garden seems to have advanced – the sown Grass Excedingly poor & The Natural Grass not got up at all in most places, & the Bear Seed not near finishd. Some Radish ready

10th Rain the whole day

11th fair & the Air more soft

12 the same & every thing made more progress & advanced more this last four days then they did for weeks before this day been Able to want a Fire Most of the Day -

13 & 14 a great deal more Rain & not warm – Snow in Cromar –

15 fair & windy – The Gin Tree in full Blosom & the Strawberries Pears & Aples & Plumbs on the Wall fully Blown & One Standard Pear Tree – Spinage Ready – Many of the Cattle dying this year for want of food & the same Complaints from England & Irland –

16 dry Cold Air with great Frost at Night 17 foggy a good showr of Rain in the Evening – from this to the 22d fine warm suney Days – the Birch & almost every Tree Except the Ash – may now be said to be in full Leaf – & not till now – The Ash will only be a few days Latter then the other Trees – Some Cherries set & some pears on the Wall – Some Goosberries the Size of Peas Standerd Aples not Blown yet Except the Oslen

23d Excedingly warm, dry sunshin 24th the Ash mostly in Leaf – 25 Warm & a high Wind – 26 Rain & a good deal of Thunder – The Standerd Trees now all in full Blosom [this Flowrish was fully formd & seemd to want only a few fine days to bring it out the End of April] The Peas in full Blosom – the Clover in the Garden Cut doun Feald Turnip sown some day ago.

from this to the 1th Jully modreat warm weather with some Rain Every Day – The Laburnum & Rane and Lylick in full Blosom & the Hathorn – the Crop & Grass much mended – from the 1th to the 7 dry weather rather Cold, one showr of hail but no frost. Standard Trees still in flowrish – the same weather to the 12th when we had Rain & warmer Air – 13 more Rain 14 mild Air & showrs – Hay Crop very good –

from that to the 19th Cold Air & drying Wind & some frost at Night. 20th very warm & hot sun – to the 24 the same – Plenty of Strawberries & Green Peas ready – & Turnip

26 some Rain frost at night Warm & dry with frost at night till the 29 – from this to the End of the Month very Cold Air & skifs of Rain always a little frost at Night – Cabage at Table.

Augst 1th Rain & thick fogg 2d some showrs – from this to the 6 dry & mild Air the 7 heavey Showrs 8 Voilent Rain the whol day – 9 Rain & Loud Wind the whole day & very Cold 10th the same 11 12 13th pritty fair but Cold 14 Rain & wind the whol day

15 pritty fair 16 most Voilent Rain the Whol day; and all night & next day. A Storm of Wind & showrs of Rain – all the haughs on Dee & Don were overflowd & much corn intirely Spoild & several Bridges carried away & much Hay spoild –

from this to the 23d the Air a little warmer & only some flying showrs & a good deal of wind – that day Rain all the afternoon

August 1782

24 most heavy Rain most of the day & some Thunder at a Distance frost at night 25 Rain the Whol afternoon & succeded by a Tempest of wind all night and most of next day, but not so Cold as last Storm from this to the 30 Cold wind & Showrs every day & Frost at Night – the Leaves of some of the Ash & Plain quit weathered – they have just been in full Beauty two Months.

4th Septr much the same weather 5 & 6 pritty warm & suny Days but Frost or Cold Dews at Night – Seid a few stooks Bear Cutt at Hatton of Fintry – all the Corn quit Green – to the 10th very Foggy the sun Breaking out in the hight of the Day, but frost or very Cold along with them at Night –

from the 10 to the 14 pritty dry but frost at Night – That Day begun to Cut doun a little park of Bear Petatoes pritty Large here no Fruit Come to any size & very Few of them – some Strawberrie Aple Rip, but quit smal – from the 14th to the 19 pritty Dry but Cold & frost at night 20 some showrs of Hail & Rain & Sever frost at Night 21th & 22d Rain & foggy – little of the Bear Crop Cut Doun & the Corns in General quit Green.

from this till the 1th Octr hardly one Day without Rain with wind & very Cold, & little sun shine – the Corns very little Changd in there Colour. 2d fair 3d Rain the whol Day 4th some showrs 5 & 6 fair & suney – got oor Bear into the Yard, but not very Dry 9 Peas Cut Doun 13 Cold weather & flying showrs every day since the 4th much of the Corns still Green – the Bear not near Cut doun & very little in the Yard in Most places – where very Early some little bits of Corn Cut - Peas taken in 15th –

from this to the 19 no Rain, little Sunshin but a good of wind.

this Day Exceding Cold. Voilent showrs of Snow & wind along with them & at night sever frost & the grownd whit – 20 Snowd the most of the day – Our Corns hardly Changd in the Colour & much of the Corns as Green as Grass very little of the Crop in General throw the whole Country Cut Doun & got in – 21th Showrs of Rain, & the Snow here mostly gon – but the Hills quit Coverd with Snow – 22 & 23 fair 24 the ground quit hard with frost, but dry most of the Day
——

Every body now Cutting doun & taking in as quick as they Can – Rip or Green – as there can be no hopes of its ever being better – a good deal snow still in the Hills – 25th a very Loud wind at Night, begun this Morning to Cut some Green Corn, but stopt by Rain – 26 a fine Day & every body Bussie Shearing, 27th the same 28 Rain in the Morning pritty fair throw the Day & Cutting Doun, but a great deal of Rain all Night. 29th Rain & wind all Day – a fall of Snow at Night – 30th & 31 Showrs of Snow & Voilent wind, & sever Frost –

1th Novr the same, the Ground Coverd with Snow, & sever Frost. 2d a fair Morning, & Cutting doun the Corn out amongst the Snow. the 7 Every Day since 2d Snow & sever Frost, all work put a stop too – 8th fair & frost – 9th took in to the Yard what Corns was Cut doun – fair all day & frost – Every body Beatting the Snow of the Stuff, & putting it in smal hutts – 10 heavy Sky & a smal drisling Rain - Every body Obligd to tak in & thresh out for there Beasts, dry the Corns, & Mill it imediatly, as it will not keep -

1782 Novr

11th all the Snow gon – Rain the most of the day, 12th heavey Rain snow & hail, & Excedingly Cold.

The 3d 4th & 5 of this Month the Mercury rose 15 degrees –

13th fair – & Every Body Cutting doun, 14th Rain the most of the Day, 15 & 16 Rough Blowing weather with Skiffs of Showrs, but all Bussie Cutting doun -

17th the same. 18 much the same, but more Rain, 19th a fine Day, & oor Corns all Cut doun, & some taken in. 20 a great Whit frost, but a little taken in afternoon – 21th a fine Day, but frost – Spreading out & Binding up – 22 & 23 very Blowing weather, with frost. a great deal taken in – 24th the same – 25 a heavy fall of Snow. 26 a fair day –

Left Disblair – Some of oor Corn not got in, much to Cut doun, &

few places that all is got in – 27 fair & frost 28 Raind the whol day –
Snow in the Hills –

from this till the 8 Decr fair Closs Weather & frost. the stacks all
Heating – & still some to Cut doun, in many Places – Some Hill touns
above Monymusk hardly begun to Cut doun – hardly any Plughing don
any where – 18 still the same weather hard frost & sunshine passing the
River Don on the Ice, no work don any where, & still some Corn not
Cut doun – this day some Rain & freshness –

from the 18th to the 26 fine fresh open weather, with a brisk Wind
– which has don great good very little of the Crop in General giveing
above half Meal, & a great deal not that. the Bear in many places will
not Cume to Make Malt. 28 & 29 Some snow

from that to the 4th of Jan^r 1783 Frost. 5th a good deal of Rain –
the Meal giveing 18 pence the peck in the Cellars & the best Meal in
the Market 20 pence the peck –

from the 5th to the 10th fine open weather. Some showrs of
Rain, but mostly Windy Weather – The Same Continowd, only some
Nights Frost, till the 16, when it Snowd a little, 17th more snow 18 &
19th a great deal of Snow with Blowing, & sever Frost, which Stopt all
traveling with wheel Carriges for some Days. It Continowd sever Frost
& showrs of Snow till the 24th when it Came fresh, & Raind most of
that Day. the Thaw Continowd - sometimes Rain & some Nights Frost
till the 2^d Feb^r – Some Plughing got don – but much of the Snow lying
& Bad traveling –

1783

Bear & Fother commonly giveing 20 pund Scotch the Boll – Some
smal Stacks at Tillery give 42 Shillings St^r the Boll – Oats & Fother
gives 18 pund Scotch the Boll – Malt 20 pence the peck, Meal now
16^d the peck – Flowr not very Fine but sweet & good at 16 pence the
peck – good whit peas for seed or Bread at 5/6 the Bushel – most of
the Meal this year sandy & Green tasted. Much of the Bear will not
Cume to be Malt – the Genral run of the Corn gives half Meal but
much of it not that _____

Feb^r 1783

from the 2 Feb^r to the 9th, much the same weather, when we
had some snow & Rain all Day here, but all Snow in the Country -

[This Day the Mercury was Observed to be Lower than it had
been for Eight Years – We heard the Great Earthquake that Messina

& Calabri Was quit destroyd with, happend the 5th & 7th of this Month
– & the 12th.]

10th Some Rain in the Morning but Cleard up a fine Day, &
the Snow here all gon. from the 10 to the 14th Rain & thick heavey
Weather, 15 16 & 17th fine Clear suney Days – with a little Frost at
Night – 18th some Rain & heavey Air – from this to the 23d dry &
some days high wind, but so sever a Frost along with it as to stop
Plughing. this day a heave fall of Snow 24 more Snow & strong Frost
25 showrs of Snow & Blowing. 26 & 27 Mild & the Snow Melting a
littel in the hight of the Day – 28 the same.

March 1th A new fall of snow, as much as at first. 2d more snow
& sever Frost. 3d Frost with some Showrs of Snow – 4th & 5 sever
Frost with a most Voilent storm of Wind, & almost as Cold as Can
be fealt here. 6th the same all from the South East.

---

three Ships drove in on the sands, Loaded with Meal, Seed Oats
& Flowr – Out of 900 Bolls of Meal, only 230 saved undamaged –

---

7 the wind a little Abated, Sleit & Snow most of the day, from
this to the 13th Clear Suneshin with frost – the Snow much gon with
the heat of the sun about toun, but still a great deal in the Country,
& the fare Hills as whit as any time this Winter.

from this to the 18 the weather More Mild, & only one night
Frost, & work going on – Some Oats sowd in Behalve – this day a
high wind – from this to the 21th the same fine weather – Oats sowd
at Disblair 24 the same weather pritty dry, & little frost – till this day
when we had a high wind with Snow & hail 25 some heavey Showrs
of Snow.

from this to the 28 Rain Every day – this Night so Sever a
frost the Locqh quit hard Froze over 29 Snow & hail 30 a Mild
day Thunder in the Night & Rain 31 More Rain —

April 1th Came out of toun a Soft Day, as warm as in june, 2d 3d
4th & 5th the same, Every Body Sowing & the Grass looking Greener
then in the End of this Month last Year – Some Spring Flowrs Blown,
& the Goosberries putting out there Leaves, all Sowd here, Except the
Low Ground. Peas Sowd – & Petatoes Plantd 8 still the same weather,
fine dry warm Sunny Days – but a little Frost at Night. The Mercury
remarkly high 9th all the Low Grownd sown – Every body fare throw
with there Oat Seed, Except where there is much to labour.

12th the Same weather – begun this day to sow the Bear Park. The Grass all looking quit Green & fine, some fealds of Oats looking Green. Plumb Flowrish quit Blown – Some Goosberrie Bushes in Leaf – Oat Seed near finishd every way – The Snow off the fare Hills. Grass Seeds Sowd doun with Oats – Gray Peas Sowd

1783 April

Petatos from England set the 21 March
Petatoes from Banff 14 April

15th from the first of this Month only one smal Showr of Rain, all dry & warm as june – this day some Flying Showrs with more wind & the Air Colder 16 the same 17-18-19 Dry & Suney with a good Brize of Wind – Larx quit Green, Goosberrie, Curran, & Rasp in Leaf – Pear flowrish fully Blown – Buds on the Birk Green,

Oat Seed don Every way, & a good deal in Brier – & several people has Bear above Ground. Every body going on with there Bear Seed –

20 Loud wind with Showrs of hail – at Fintray that day Young Latice of this years Sowing & Radish at Table. Peas of this Year Stringd & will be soon in Blosom, French Beans far advanced, Cherrie Trees in full Blowsom – the Buds of the Plain Tree Burst, & Showing there Leaf tho not Expanded.

Letters from Paris Dated 29 March says we have Snow here just now

---

21 very Cold Loud wind with Showrs of Rain & hail – from this to the 29th Cold hard dry Air, with a good deal of wind & some nights frost – This Day much warmer, & a fine sweet mild Showr of Rain – Bear Seed finishd in the Park - 30 Warm with some Showrs of rain & a thick fogg at Night –

1th May a thick fogg in the Morning but Cleard up a fine Day but not so warm – Larx now in full Beauty, the Hathorn green, & many of the Plain Trees the Leaf quit Expanded. the Trees of the Birch that are Young the Leaf Penny Broad – Fruit Trees on the Wall Pears Plumbs Aples & Cherries the flowrish quit Blown. Grass & Brier looking fine – Goosberries & Currans in full Leaf, & flowrish - 2d 3d & 4th Cold Air & some flying Showrs – The 5th in the morning a heavey fall of Snow but soon Melted - Showrs of Snow & hail with wind all the Day (in England the same weather) –

6th & 7th 8 & 9th high Wind with Showrs of hail & Snow & frost at Night – The Bear Seed here all finishd with the Grass Seed Sown & Rolld – not one Showr that has any way wat the ground since 1ᵗʰ Apr the Snow made no impression in many places Bad Seed sown & the Ground Plowghd over again for Bear – & many Complaints of the Seed coming up thin. great importations of Peas for Meal – Corn for Seed & Bread & Bear Dᵒ flowr Cheap, the fine Flowr at 16 pence the peck Oat Meal 18ᵈ – Peas Meal 1/ Bear Dᵒ 1/2 Malt 1/11ᵈ–

The 10ᵗʰ Early in the Morning a good heavey Rain quit Calm & warm which wat the Ground – the 11ᵗʰ a high wind & great drowght which took of all the good Effects we hoped for from the Rain

15 Still high wind & great drowght – The grass & Brier not looking so well as it did a week agoe Radish often at Table 16 the Evening a Showr of Rain, & the Air warmer, 17 high wind again & drought.

1783 May

18 & 19 the same with smal flying Showrs & very Cold & some frost at Night 20 warmer but still not the lest appearence of Rain which is much Wanted as a great deal of the grain sown lys unsprung 21ᵗʰ the Air Warm & hot Sunshin –

A Larg Sallet at Table – Some Blosom on the Peas, Aples & Pears – Knotted Goosberries & Currans. All the Trees except the Ash in full Leaf & Glory.

22ᵈ high wind with frequent Showrs & very Cold 23ᵈ the same Some Showrs of Snow in the Morning the fare Hills Coverd with Snow 24 Exceding Cold & at Night so Sever a Frost as took off the Tops of the Early Petatos

25 26 27 Still Cold with some Frost at Night – flying Showrs & windy throw the Day 28, 29ᵗʰ bitter Cold & winds high Dark heave sky – 30 still Cold with a drizling Rain, 31 the Air Softer

June 1ᵗʰ & 2ᵈ fair 3ᵈ & 4ᵗʰ thick fogg, & driziling Rain – from this to the 9 dry & windy, that Day a Showr 10 Several parsial Sowrs & some Thunder – the 11ᵗʰ a good heavey fall of Rain most of the Day – 12 heavey Sky & Cold but no Rain 13 the same – 14ᵗʰ a Smal Rain all afternoon which came on more heavey & Raind all Night & next Day but still Cold & wind with it, & Constant foggs. Eat Smal Turnip here & Goosberries for Tarts – the Ash Tree in Leaf – Many of the Trees foxd & Spoild with the frost & Cold wind_____

16ᵗʰ from 7 to 9 Oclock a Most Tremendious Storm of Thunder & Lightning with heavey rain Accompanyd with a Loud Wind which I never heard befor, with so Loud thunder – the Rain & wind continowd till Night – 17 thick fogg & Smal Rain the Air a good deal Warmer.

from this to the 22ᵈ the Air heavey with foggs most of the Day - this Day Clear & warm Sune.

The Bear Crop looking well every way, but the Corns in most places looking very Bad, only a stalk here & there – quit run over with Grass & Weeds – Except where the English Oats was Sown. the Grass Crop very poor. the haugh on Don where our best corn Usd to be Worce then Any – & the River been over a great deal of them – the Crop in Genral looking better by Kemnay & Monymusk then from this to Abd – _____

from the 22 june to the End Exceding Warm Soft Aire with foggs or Dews all Night & Day & some Showrs which has mended the whol Crop past what could have been lookd for -

1ᵗʰ & 2 Jully exceding Warm – 3ᵈ from one Oclock in the Morning to 10 oclock a Continowd Storm of Thunder & Leghtning with some heavey Showrs of Rain after that a high Wind. from this to the 7ᵗʰ high wind, & warm Air & thick fogg – _____

have Eat Some Strawberries Green Peas twice at Table, & Artichokes – turnip often. Our Bees Swarmd 26 june, & again 5 Jully - & again 9ᵗʰ Jully – no fruit this year here – & Goosberries & Currans quit destroyd with Catterpiler, the Common Fir Tres quit Bared of there foilege with them, & all the Fruit & other Trees much hurt. The Crop now so much mended that where we thought no Crop Could be it looks tolarable – the rest fine – Early Bear quit Shot – Petatoes been Eat in many Places, & the Grass Crop better then Could have been thought – _____

Jully 1783

the 10ᵗʰ the same weather fogg most of the day – 11ᵗʰ Thunder at a Distance in the Morning, Closs Air & fogg all Day – at Eleven oclock night, the Thunder begun again & continoud pritty Loud with a vast deal of Leghtning till 2 oclock in the Morning of the 12ᵗʰ. This day Vastly warm the foggs still Continow Some People Says there has not been a Day since the 3ᵈ but they have heard Thunder – This & such a Continouance of thick fogg is uncommon in this Country.

The Leavs of the Corn & Bear is Yellowed, & the Tops of the Petatoes Blackned – from what caus We know not as nobody will alow of any frost having been. the Most of the Broom Bloom too is Weathred _____

The Mercry here keeps very high We hear from London the Weather is Sultry hot & the Barometer in the Shad at Midday has been above Eighty degrees & one Day near ninety which is hotter then under the Line. _____

from the 12ᵗʰ to the 18ᵗʰ Exceding Hot, Closs Air & Constant foggs. The Same to the 21th when we had Thunder at a distance all the Morning & Rain. The fogg Still Continouing all Day & at Night Loud Thunder with most heavey Rain 22 & 23 the Sky Clearer but still Exceding Hot 24 Some wind & Rain in the Evening 25 fogg & hot 26 Clear Sky & a Voilent wind.

Our Hay Cut the 17th, & is now in Tramp Colls in the Yard, a fine Crop – Some Bear Cut near Abd. & Some begining to chang Colour in the Country – never was a finer Crop of Bear Seen. 27 a Clear Sky, & Showrs of Rain thick fogg at Night. 28th windy & Clear in the fornoon & fogg at Night – the Air much Cooler. 29 Clear Sky & some wind [Bear Cut] 30th a good deal of fogg 31th for 2 Hours in the Morning a Voilent Storm of wind the rest of the Day Calm & pritty Clear.

The Thunder We had the 3d Jully was very Universal over all England & the South of Scotland & Houses Much hurt & a good Many People Killd – What we had on the 11th they had most severly on the 10th & a deal of hurt by it – the Thunder we had the 21th did a great deal damage about Newcastle & many other parts in England the same day 31 in Kent they had Thunder & the most remarkable Lightinng. We had Thunder & heave Rain 2d August & a great Chang in the feel of the Air from Very hot to Cold * 8 the Moon had such firey Apearence & Shap throw the fogg we thought her a Larg Muir Burn. 18 a Ball of Fire with a long tail movd slowly from North to South.

1th August pritty Clear the hight of the Day, Thick fogg in the Evening.

2d Thunder & heavey Rain in the Morning & thick fogg all day

3d a great deal more Rain the fogg still Continows

4 & 5th the Air much Colder but the foggs still the same Oor Hay put up recon to have more then 4 hunder Ston off the Acre

6 Rain all the for part of the Day

7 Rain in the afternoon

8 fair & Clear Sky, * moon 9 Rain all the afternoon

10 a good Brisk wind & Clear Sky

11 & 12 Rain in the afternoon

Aug 1783

13 fair & exceding Cold, & Clear Sky – Bear Cut doun Every way –

14 warmer & foggy again

15 very warm & heavey Rain

16 thick fogg & Closs Air

17 a pritty Clear day

18 & 19 thick fogg & Thunder

20 a fine Clear day but very warm, Seed at Rayne & several other places good Large Stacks of Bear, & pritty Genral Hearvest all round that – there Crop much further advancd then here.

21 Rain & thick fogg – Distant Thunder

22 Still thick fogg & some Skiffs of Rain

23 a fine Clear day

24 heavey Sky & Showrs, 25th the same 26 & 27 Constant Rain & thick heavey Sky – 28 Some Showrs in the Morning, but a fine afternoon begun to Cut doun oor Bear – still fogg

29 fogg but fair, & a good deal wind. Every body Cutting doun Bear – Cut most of oors & oor whit Peas

30 & 31th pritty fair but still foggs

1th Septr Cut doun most of oor English Oats a Clear fine Day but Fogg at Night 2 Thick fogg to the Door with Rain & some wind – at Night the Air full of Stars & a little Frost

3d Morning fair with wind – from 12 to 6 oclock Voilent Rain, & thunder at a great Distance – at Night Clear & full of Stars, with pritty Dancers Like Frost – The Air not two hours in the Same Stat – warm & Cold alternatly. Every body Alarmd for the Crop as most of the Corns is Still very Green, Except English Oats.

4 & 5 pritty fair – Cut doun some more Peas & the rest of oor Bear & English Oats.

6 fair in the Morning, took in some Bear – from 12 oclock to Night Voilent Rain & wind 7th Showrs of Rain

8 Thunder & Showrs of Rain

9 Some Showrs 10th a fine Day

11 dry with some Wind got in all oor Bear, English Oats, & whit peas – a great frost that morning.

12 had Rain all Night & all Day with Thunder in the forenoon pritty Loud – Frost at Night

13 Some Rain – 14 Constant Rain & wind. 15 Loud Wind with some flying Showrs. Cut doun some Oats – 16 Still the same Every body Cutting doun & taking in – Frost Every Night

17 & 18 fine Days bright Sun & some Wind – took in what Oats was Cut the 15th

19 thick fogg & Rain

20th Some Showrs 21 dry & windy

22d a Storm of Wind & Rain all Night, & all day wind Continowd with Showrs

23 a fine Clear day 24 the same 25 Windy with Showrs –

1783 Sept^r

Bear Crop & English Oats got in almost every way, & a fine Crop of both – New Bear Meal at 6^d & 7 pence in the Market, but much of oor own Country Oats to Cut doun not being Ripe & much beat doun with heavey Rains & wind _____

from 25 to 29 dry & warm with thick fogg in afternoon, & frost at Night took in this day what more Oats was Cut doun –

2^d Octr fine Dry Suney Days & Frost at night

3^d Rain the whol day & a Loud wind – Cutting doun some more Oats – much Corn not Ripe yet – 5 6 & 7th very high wind (took in what was Cut doun the 4th) 8th the Ground whit with Snow but soon Melted & hard frost at Night

9 a fine warm Suney day but Snow on the fare Hills – Cut doun the last of oor Corn – in some Places there Corns very Green, & little Cut doun, in Early Places hervest don - [Malt now at 15 pence the peck] 10th & 11 fine days, & no frost. 12th Blowing 13 thick & foggy from that to the 18 Warm fine Suney Days & little frost – one Day some Thunder

In every place where the Corns Come up thin & was keept long back by oor Sever Month of May, the Crop is Exceding poor. 30 threve will hardly Yeald a Boll – other places where good seed & sooner sown, there Cannot be a finer Crop. _____

to the 22^d much the same weather Continoud. this day Cold & Blowing, with some Showrs of hail – 23^d a good deal of Rain, & Snow in the fare Hills 24 & 25 pritty fair but Cold & hard frost at Night 26 very Cold with Rain from this to the 29 Cold & windy but fair & Bright Sunshine frost at Nights 30 the Same, a great deal of Lightning at Night 31th Rain

Novr 1th & 2^d Thick & foggy 3^d the Same with Rain – heavy Gloomy Sky, but fair to the 6th – The Same to the 9th without any frost – this day Clear & frost – the Same weather to the 12 when We had a little Snow & Sever frost at Night 13 Some more Showrs of Snow 14 & 15 So Sever a frost that the Watter Urie was froze over in one Night & done very near Closs in Some places – That day Came in to Abd. 16 fresh & a heavey Rain – from this to the 23 fine open weather – the Cattle Still getting food all day in the fealds, & Plughing almost done 30th Still the Same open fine weather – this day a very high wind & Rain -

Oat Meal 14^{d}½ & Bear Meal 9 pence the peck

Decr 8th Still fine open weather only one day Rain since the 1th

17 Still the Same Weather 22 the same weather Continoud

25 & 26th. This Voilent Storm from the East drove one Ship on Shore at Don Mouth. The Master & Mate Lost, & two Ships betwixt this & Stonhaven, all on Board of both Ships Perishd

27 the wind abated but Snow most of the day. the Snow very deep & hardly any traveling with wheel Carriges the Post from this to Oldmeldrum 12 miles was 9 Hours on the Road – from the 27th to the 31th Showrs of Snow & the Kinest frost we have seen for many Years no heat of the Room makes any impresion on the Ice on the inside of the Windows the Watter in a Bason Froze in half an hour at 10 oclock fornoon tho a good fire in the Room

Janr 1784

the 1th Janr 1784 the Air Milder 2d a good deal of wind and drift – at Night a most Voilent Storm of wind at South East – this Hurrican of Wind Blowd all the Snow into Such Wreaths as was never Seen in this Country Many of them 18 foot perpindicular Many People was two Days in there Houses befor they Could be Cast so as to let them out – all traveling Except on foot put a Stop to – at the Cove, & Several other little Harbours near this great peaces of the Rocks was rent off & thrown into there Harbour, the Sea Came out 40 Yards further then the Oldest Man Ever remembers, & a great deal of Lightning along with the Wind – which Continowd the 3d all Day – Many Houses in the Country was unroofd & Stacks of Corn & Hay Carried off –

The frost of the 31 was most remarkable the Thermometr fell 5½ degrees below the frizing point – roots of all kinds was froze, Bear in Cask & bottle Large jars of Pepermint Watter all most all, House flowr roots & Plants was Killd it only Continowd So intence for 20 or 24 Hours So very Sever _____

the 4th it Thawd, & Still a good deal of wind - the 5, 6 & 7th Frost & Clear weather, Except Sudden foggs that Comes on in a moment – Sometimes stays an Hour, Sometimes not 5 Minuts & this has often been throw all the winter _____

11th Still the Same weather, no more Snow – the High ways Cast & mostly made passible that the Post Comes in now regularly – & roads Cast to Mills, which has been mostly Laid since the Voilent frost – 12th fresh, & the Air Soft – from this to 17th a Continowd Thaw – the River Brok, & Mills all going this day frost again from the 17 to the 22 Frost & Some Days very Keen but nothing to that of the 31th last Month – 22 a heavey fall of Snow no wheel Machin has been able as yet to go further on the North road then 4 Miles from this – the South road & from Buchan is open – 23d & 24th frost very keen

25 frost & Showrs of Snow 26 More Snow – 27 & 28 Still more Snow, & Sever Frost –

29 from Yesterday, a more heavey fall of Snow then we have had yet – wind still at North East & great want of Coals – the Mills all Laid & meal in the Cellars at 15 pence the peck

30th Frost 31 the Air more Mild, & wind into the West, & begins to Thaw a little.

Febr 1th a Brisk Thaw & Pritty Loud wind, Frost at Night 2d hard Frost with Loud wind & Showrs of Snow. 3d Frost Continoud till afternoon when we had a Brisk Thaw again & pritty high wind, which Continoud all Night – 4th the same 5th Some Showrs of Snow & hard Frost at Night. 6th a great deal of more Snow & Cold wind, with Frost 7 Still a More heavey fall of Snow & Cold wind –

This Snow Blown in new wreath by the wind that was along with it made traveling Still worce then ever, & Except the South Post Road there is no way a Wheel Machin Can go – the wind all this Storm has kept so much to the North that few Ships Could get from the South here, which has made Coals almost not to be got & has destressd the poor excedingly –

1784 Febr

from the 7th to the 14th only one Day without Snow Constant frost & pritty Calm the wind still in the same Art – this Day the wind got to South East & we had a Thaw with Showrs of Snow

at Night the wind in the old Art & keen frost again 15 Frost & Cold wind – 18th every day more Snow.

those little freshnesses we have had about toun has not reached the Country & the Storm much deeper then Ever, & tis no better over all England, & also in France – This Storm is thought more Sever then in the Year 40, as we have a great deal more Snow, & always incressing.

21 Feby Every day more Snow the wind last night into the South & a heave fall of Snow this day a little more Mild a Brisk Thaw at Night 22 the Thaw Still Continows & Showrs of Rain – The first Rain we have seen Since the 23 Decr –

23d More Rain & a good deal of wind & a Brisk Thaw but a little frost at Night –

24 a great deal of Rain

25 a fine Clear Suney Day the Rivers all Brok & the Snow going away 26 the Same 27 Cold with Some Rain & the wind into the North again. 28 & 29 Sever Frost a Showr of Hail at Night

March 1th the Ground Coverd with Snow & Showrs of Snow

throut the day – frost & fair to the 4th that day fresh & foggy –

5th Showrs of Rain – the first Air Ballown Made here Set off – 6 fogg in the Morning warm & Suneshin throw the Day, & fogg at Night 7th A great deal of Rain the whol day _____

The Sholls of Ice in Don was so Large as to Choke up the uswall Bed of the River & turn it out of its Cours in three diffrent Places, at Towie, Monymusk & Kintor – & brought it doun throw there fine Haugh Grounds _____

Oat Meal 15 pence Bear Meal 10d – Corn & fother gieveing 28/4 per Boll

The 8 Heavey Rain till night when we had Snow 9th the Ground all Coverd with Snow. from the 9 to the 13th frost & sometimes Showrs of Snow or hail – that Day more Snow – the 14th the Snow more then foot Deep – Obliged to Cast a Road into the Chaple 15th, 16, 17, & 18 frost, & Sune Shine, which last has melted a good deal of the Snow here, but no warmth or Mildness in the Air

19 the Same 20th & 21 the Air more Soft, the Same to the 24 with some smal Showrs of Rain. Ploughs now begining to go in Many Places.

This Storm has been almost Universal. At Paris they never Experenced any thing like it. When it Brok up the begining of March the Seiane Rose 22 feet above its Bed, did much Damage & Boats was Obliged to go in Several of the Streets of Paris – in Irland the poor was almost famishd, there Petatos being so much Spoild by the intence frost. in Germany Villages Sweept a way, & many Lives Lost by the Brake of the Storm. The Rhine did infinite hurt by its overflowing –

26 March a new fall of Snow with Sever frost which the Sune and Lenth of the Day made little impression on

1784 March

27 Sever Frost & Showrs of Hail 28 at Night a New fall of Snow 29 & 30 hard Frost 31 More Snow with a pritty high wind & Sever Frost such as to Freze a little watter in a Bason in a Room

April 1th more Snow 2d fair with frost. Rain at Night 3 & 4 Rain & Slitt 5 the Air warmer & a grate deal of Rain 6 7 & 8 pritty dry & Suney 9 Cold with a great deal of Rain & Snow 10 & 11th Cold with Some Showrs of Snow

Monday the 12 Came out to Disblair

Snow in the Morning but a fine Suney Day – no Mark of Vegetation the whole way. Here a few Crocuses, & Some Spring flowrs, & Some Peas sown befor Winter above Ground

13 a great fall of Snow 14 dry & Cold 15 Exceding Cold with Loud

wind & Rain 16th pritty fair 17 more Rain 18th dry & no frost 19 the same Sowd Peas in the feald, & some Oats –

20th a fine Day, the wind into the West, & no frost. Work doing in the fealds & Garden Every body is now Sowing any bit of Ground tolarably dry, but very little don yet any way. the Snow not quit gon in the Hill above Fintray the Near Hills Spoted & the fare distant Hills as Whit as ever

21th the wind in to the North East again, with fogg & Rain 22 a great deal of Snow. from this to the 26 Snow every day & frost & as Cold as when the Storm was lying on the Ground, which the hight of the Sun, & Lenth of the Day, prevents. little work Can go on, & Every thing as Winter

27 & 28 Sowd the rest of what Oats was to be Sowd here. Sad work, but every body now sowing if posible – Throw dispair Snow & hail every day and Hard Frost at Nights 30 April the same weather Continoud this day a great deal of Rain – oor Petatos was planted the 28

May 1th Cold with Showrs, & frost at Night. not a Flowrish bud Burst on any Tree. Some Leaves begining on the Goosberrie Bushes not a Larch Changd its Colour nor a Bud so much as Green on the Birch, or Hathorn

2, 3 & 4 of May the Air Milder a good Brize of Wind & no frost at Night, 5th the same, Oor Lint Sown the Ground wonderfully dryd, & everything makeing great Progress – The 6 Some Smal Showrs of Rain the first of oor Bear Sown.

7th 8, 9 th the same fine weather & no frost. the Cukow heard this day for the first time – Every body Except in the Hill touns, don with Oat Seed, & now Bussie to get there Bear into the Ground. there is Some Oat Briar up – the Sown Grass all looking Green. the Larch fare advancd, & some of them quit Green – the Goosberrie Bushes almost fully Leafd – & some Pear Blosom out –

13th Still the Same weather – & only one Night frost – this Day & at Night a good Deal of Rain 14th, 15th, & 16 fine Mild Sunney Days – the Lint all above Ground the Oat Briar all up round here & looking Surprisingly well & Clean, Grass looking fine The Larch in high Glory the Birch Leaf on Some Trees penny Broad the Leaf on Some Plains now Expanded, the Beach out, & Elm – Some on the Hathorn Flowrish on Wall Trees the Plumb Cherrie Aple & Pears all opend – This Day fortnight one Could not have known a Flowrish from a Leaf Bud but those well aquanted with them.

1784 May

The 18th still the same weather Some days Excedingly warm

19 & 20 Colder with Loud wind & a little touch of Frost at night

21 & 22 Milder but a great drowght & Rain much wishd for - Most of the Bear Seed don & a great deal above Ground

23ᵈ & 24ᵗʰ the Same, 25 Some Skifs of Rain 26 a good deal of Rain & two pritty Loud Claps of Thunder with Lightning – all the Trees now in full foilige & the Ash pritty well advanced.

from this to the 1ᵗʰ June Cold Air with high wind & Some touches of frost at Night, & Showrs of Rain – this day a Calm & Milder Air

2ᵈ Calm & foggy – the Flowrish now out on the Standard Trees – the Gin & wall Trees Lossing there Flowrish & the Fruit begining to Sett Cherries pritty Large – The Peas that Came throw the winter Showing there Flowrish – in some places the Bear Seed hardly finishd yet –

from this to the 7ᵗʰ Suney Days with a fogg, or Cold Dwe at Night. this Day Cold Air & heavey Sky – the Peas now in full Blosom – 8 the Same & very Cold. 9ᵗʰ the Air Softer & Rain the most of the Day with some Distant Thunder – 10 very Cold heavey foggy Sky with Rain the whol day – 11ᵗʰ more Rain & Frost at Night – 12 dry & Suney but Cold 13 more Rain & Still Cold Air –

20 the Same weather – Still very Cold with Rain, every day Loud wind, & frost at Night. The Leaves of the Peas all spekeld with Frost – & the foilege of the Trees much hurt – Spinig Several times at Table Sallet Ready 23ᵈ Still the Same weather – 28 the Same weather, so Cold as not able to want fire, & frost at Night – Turnip Seed finishd – 29 the Same weather, 30 & 1ᵗʰ Jully –

2ᵈ the Air Milder, 3ᵈ warm & Sunshin, the same weather to the 8ᵗʰ a good deal rain that Day. 9 dry – Oor hay all Cut doun that Crop in Many Places not good Especialy where Drifts of Snow lay Longest – Turnip all gon wrong – Obliged to be Sown over again, & that in many Places three times Sown – a great deal of Caterpiller & Vermin this year –

from the 9 to the 17 Blowing weather with Showrs. oor Hay mostly in Tramp Colls. Peas, Strawberries, Cherries & Artichock at Table – Eat Strawberries at Abd the 14, as very rair, & not very Rip. The 17ᵗʰ a Cold Surly Day, & Frost at Night. The 18 a warm pleasent Day, 19ᵗʰ a Vast deal of heave Rain – Blowing & Showrs to the 22ᵈ Cabage at Table. from this to the End of this Month Cold Blick surly weather, frost or Cold Dwes at Night –

August 1ᵗʰ a fine warm Suney Day – the same till the 5ᵗʰ, The Hay put in Sow – 6ᵗʰ Cold with Some Showrs 7ᵗʰ & 8 the Same, the Ground whit with frost Early in the morning of the 9ᵗʰ, Showrs throw the Day – from this to the 11th warm & Suney – from the 11 to the 16 dry weather Some days very Cold & others warmer & Suney. this day very Cold & flying Showrs – often frost & Cold Dwes at Night – from this to the 23 dry & Sunney Days, but Seldom warm. 24 Bitter Cold & Surly with Some flying Showrs 27 Still the Same weather & last Night a Sever frost Some Stucks of Bear cut Doun in diffrent parts, but the Crop in Genral very Green – Some Early Aples rip here – from this to the 30 a good deal of Rain Every Day & last night a great frost & this Day Exceding Cold – The Lint pulld – fine Crop

1784 August

31th at Kemnay very little Cut doun there, or on the Watter Sid but the Crop looking more forward – in most Places the Tops of the Petates taken off with the Frost –

1th Septr Still very Cold with Flying Showrs. 2^d the Air much Milder 3^d a warm Suney Day with a good deal of wind – 4 & 5th the same fine weather 12th Still the same fine weather Continoud – we have not had so much Summer since May – Some Bear Cut doun Every way & some Early English Oats – but no Constant hervest any way – & the Oat Crop in Genral very Green Still for all this most favourable Weather – This Day some Rain

13th thick & drizling 14 the same 15 Cutt doun oor Bear a fine Day 16 & 17 the Same 18 a little Rain, but Every body Cutting doun 19 a Loud wind & hevey Sky – the Crop Come much quicker forward then could have been Expected, & Constant Hervest in Many Places – this Night a heave Rain 20 more Rain 21th fair & a great frost at Night 22 pritty good day 23 very Cold & flying Showrs 24 fair 25 26 & 27 foggy with some Rain 28 Cut doun Some Corn 29 & 30 took in all the Bear & Peas dry days with frost at Night

1th Octr 2 & 3 Blowing Weather with Skifs of Showrs & a great deal of Rain & Calm – 5 a high wind – from the 5th to the 12 dry weather quit Calm no frost, & no Sun – oor Oats Cut doun – Except one peace of English Oats, which is quit Green – In Early dry Ground Hervest don – in most places not half throw – the Bear all in every way – Oat Meal giving 13^d½ the peck & Bear Meal is giving 8^d½ the peck ⸻

from the 12th to the 19th no Rain & quit calm – this day a Showr with some wind & frost at Night 20 & 21th fair with some wind got in all that was Cutt doun – 22 Showrs & frost at Night 23^d a good Showr of Snow

The Oat Meal in the Market the 22^d at 10^d½ the peck – not from the Prospect of great plenty but want of Money to pay Rent

24th Showrs of Snow & hail Showrs the whole day & the Ground hard with frost at Night to 25 Snowd the whole day – the Corns all Coverd with Snow. 26 the Snow Still lying – quit Calm & thick Air – Thaw at Night 27 the Same, & the Snow going off 28 the Snow gon, Calm foggy & not a Breath of wind – 29th & 30 the Same – Some frost at Night 31 the Same –

No work don Since the 23d Much to Cutt Doun & a great deal to take in. The weather being So Calm befor the Storm, & what was in not keeping incide every body afraid to take in what was Cutt – or Cutt what was not Rip –

Novr 1th Cut doun the last of oor Oats Still Calm & frost at Night – 2d the Same 3d a Brize of Wind & Every Body Cutting Doun 4 Rain. from this to the 8 some Rain every day & little wind this day fair Some wind & very Cold – 9 Wind & Some Showrs 10 more Rain frost at Night 11th a fine day, & high wind – The Mercury Exceding Low – 12 <u>got in the last of oor Oats</u> 13 the Strongest frost we have had – a Suney Day & Clear Sky

14 Morning Sever frost, Rain all the rest of the Day, & wind all Night 15 a Loud wind & fair – 16 frost & fair –

1784 Novr

all Round this taken in & mostly So Every way – Except Some very late places where they have Some to Cut doun yet – the Crop thought a very Rich one – the Meal now at 10 pence in the Cellars & 11 pence in the Market –

17 the Ground whit with Snow and Sever frost – Came into Abd – 18 frost with Showrs of Snow. the Same to the 22 –

the frost very intence Stopt all Plughing

23d the same – the Snow up the Country very deep & a Good deal of there Corns Still to take in. 24 thaw & Showrs of Rain from this to the 29 open weather Showrs of Rain & wind, 30 very Cold

Decr 1 the Ground here Coverd with Snow, & very Cold, & Sever frost 2 Showrs of Snow & Sever frost 3 the Same 4 & 5 frost 6 a fall of Snow last night Computed 8 Inches deep. This day and all Night a very high Wind 7 & 8 Sever frost with Wind & Showrs of hail – from this to the 11th Snow Every Day, the Storm very deep & traveling allmost impractable 15 Still the Same weather, Snow more or Less Every Day. 16 fresh & the Snow melting a little – from this to the 20 frost & fresh by turns 21 Sever frost & More Snow

---

The high wind of the 6 & 7 did infinit damage on the Cost of England More then a hundr Ships Stranded or lost. Some Ships lost on this Cost

22 Showrs of Snow 23 a great deal of Snow 24th & 25 fresh the Snow Melting 26 & 27 Thaw & frost by turns.

1 Janr 1785 weather the Same There has been a Closs Storm in the Country & no Thaw the Snow very deep & no traveling in Many Places in England, & at Nairn Inverness &c. the Storm much deeper then here

8 Janr much the same weather here – Some heavey falls of Snow but Soon Melted again

9 & 10 Seemd a Serious Thaw

11 Rain – 12 Frost & more Snow which soon went off & from this to the 29 fresh open weather Some Oats Sown at the Stoket & Some Potatoes Planted – The Meal in the Market giving 9d½ the peck – The 29 frost & Some Snow 30 more Snow

Febr 1th a great deal more Snow with Blowing & Sever Frost the 2d fresh & a brisk Thaw 3 Snow again 4 more Snow & as great a frost as we have had 5 & 6 frost – from this to the 17 frost & fresh by turns this last night & all this day a heavey fall of Snow, with high wind – 18 the same 19 Still Snow & high wind all night & this day

20 & 21 Still more Snow the Storm deeper then it has been all winter, but Coals Cheap & plenty, & Meal at 8 pence pr Peck

22 & 23 Strong Frost & Showrs of Snow all traveling to the North in any wheel Machin imposible 24 the wind which has been all this month at North & N East has got into the West & a kind of thaw but Frost at Night 25 the Snow Melting a little but little Mildness in the Air 26 a new fall of Snow

Febr 1785

27 & 28 th Sever frost & Showrs of Snow

March 3d Frost as Strong every day as has been all winter & little of the Snow gon 8th Still the Same – sever frost & this day Snow – no work got don Since the 29 Janr – Meal at 8 pence & 8½ pr Peck – Coals Scotch So Low as 40 pence the Boll -

9th a great deal of Snow – Several people Lost there Lives by drift & Blowing –

from this to the 15 th Sever Frost. 16 a little Softer & the Snow melting 17 the Same & looks a thorow thaw 20 the Thaw Continows a great deal of the Snow gon & Ploughs begining to go

21 frost & Showrs of Snow

22 More Snow with wind & Sever frost 23 frost & Cold 24th 25 &

26 mild & the Snow all gon 27 a good deal of Snow, & Strong frost.
28 More Snow 29 a great fall of Snow. 30 31th frost & more Snow.

April 1 the Same 2d a great deal more Snow 3d Sever frost
from this to the 11th fine dry weather & Hardly any frost
Oats Sowd at Disblair this day 12 the Same & Every body Sowing___

This winter has lasted 5 Months & 24 days – the first Snow was
23 Octr which has been all frosty & Severe Except a few days at the
End of Janauary. It has been the Same in England.

April 14th came to Disblair a fine day, all hands at work Every
way – a great deal Sowd. the spring flowrs in great Glory Peas above
Ground Sowd this year – the Larch Buds begining to look Green &
Some Pear flowrish fare advanced 16 Still the Same fine weather
17 the Same, oor Oat Seed finishd not an Air of frost Sine the
11th nor a drop of Rain Since the Storm went off - 18 Some frost a
Clear Suney day & a good deal wind 19 a Slight Showr Rain the Air
a little Colder
from this to the 24 Fine weather with Sometimes a little Rain but
nothing to Watt the Ground – the Oat Seed don in Many Places &
mostly ower every way Some Brier up – The Same to the End of the
Month.
1th May the Same Weather – a good deal of oor Bear Sowd –
Goosberries & Curran in full Leaf & Flourish Some Flowrish fully
Blown on the Plumb, Cherry, Pear & Aple. The Leaf on the Young
Birch near penny Broad – all the Larch pritty Green – the Young ones
in full Glory – Our Petatoes Planted the 25 April –
2d a hearty Showr of Rain – Dry & pritty Cold to the 5th . The
Same to the 9th, that day Some Rain, 10th fogg & drizling Showrs the
Air very Cold 11th a high wind & dry Sunny Day 15th Still no Rain &
high winds 16 a Showr of Snow. the wind very high & bitter Cold frost
at Night 17 The Same with skifs of Snow 18 The Same, the Drowght
excedingly Sever on Everything not a Showr of any kind that wats the
Ground Since the 3d April
19 a Showr of hail & Rain 20 dry – very Cold 21 a more heavey
Showr of Rain then we have yet had – The Bear Parks don, Grass
Seeds Sowd & Rolld Bear Seed mostly over Every Way_____
22 the fare Hills Coverd with Snow – very Cold & high wind
to the 25 when we had Some Rain -

1785 May
from this to the 29 the Air Milder & Showrs of Rain Every

Day This day & yesterday Thunder hear & in diffrent places

30 a great Frost with Showrs of hail & Exceding Cold. A Sellat with Radish &c at Table Some days ago _____

from 30 May to the 2ᵈ June Cold with parsial Showrs of Rain & hail – that Night so Strong a frost that all the pools was froze & the Ground all whit – 3ᵈ a good deal of Rain from that to the 9ᵗʰ Cold dry & Suney that day Showrs of Rain & warm –

Came oot of Abd – Nothing there or Round it more Advanced then here the Grass looking very ill Every way – little fruit Sett the Ash hardly in full Leaf Yet – the 10ᵗʰ the first day we Could want a fire 11 windey & not so warm the Peas in full Blosom

from this to the 15 dry Blowing weather, that day Some Rain & Every day Some Rain to the 20ᵗʰ – _____ The Turnip Sowd 18ᵗʰ

25 & 26 Bees Swarmd _____ from 20ᵗʰ to the 30ᵗʰ the Hotest weather we have had for Several years, & not a drop Rain

1ᵗʰ Jully not quit so warm

2ᵈ Rain most of the day –

Peas, Cabage & Backd Goosberries at Table & Young Turnips – Tasted Strawberries & Cherries –

in the hott weather, the Trees had all a Shineing on the Leaves, as laid ouer with a Rich Syrop & tasted as Sweet, it dropd from them – & the weeds was Laid ouer with it – The Plain, Birch, Lauburnum & Beach was all in that State but no fruit Trees, Ash, or Firr had any thing of it.

---

to the 8 fine Weather not so warm & some Showrs The 9ᵗʰ & 10 Excedingly Cold with Some Rain 11 & 12 Milder. The Hay Cutt 13 & 14 fine Mild weather – all the Bear Shot – Artichocks Cutt

from this to the 23 fine pleasant weather – in Many diffrent places Loud Thunder & heavey Rain but non here 24 some little Sweet Showrs, 25 & 26 warm & Suney – 27 a heavey Rain and Continoud all night – 28 & 29 fine warm dry days – Petatoes at Table

from this to the 9 August foggy weather & Rain most Every Day to the 15 a great deal of Rain, hardly one Day quit fair Since this Month began. The same weather to the 22ᵈ that day fair & Suney, but Rain at night – Every day Rain to the 27 That morning the ground whit with Frost – often frost in the Night throw all this Month – Some Bear Cut doun in diffrent places – 28 Rain –

from this to the 3ᵈ Septʳ every day Rain 7ᵗʰ every day heavey
Rain & mostly frost at night

8ᵗʰ begun to Cut <u>Bear</u> but was Stopd by the Rain 9 a pritty fair day
but Rain at Night & all the 10ᵗʰ Raind Closs, & thick fogg. 11 Rain in
the Morning, & the fogg Continoud 12 a fine fair day Cut the Rest of
the <u>Bear</u> 13 the Same Every body Cutting doun 14 fair but thick fogg
Morning & Evening

15 a thick fogg with Rain 16 & 17 hot & Suney quit calm Cut
doun Some <u>Corns</u> 18 thick fogg & drizling Rain the whole day 19
the Same 20 & 21ᵗʰ pritty dry Cut doun a park of Corn

Septʳ 1785

22ᵈ Cold & Showrs 23ᵈ a Strong frost – Hills whit with Snow –
& most bitter Cold 24 a Tempest of wind & voilent Rain the whole
day – the Watter Don all over the Haughs – from this to the 29 high
wind & Constant Showrs & Cold as winter that day & the 30 dry got
in some Bear

Octʳ 1 a good wind & some flying Showrs <u>took in the rest of the
Bear</u> 2ᵈ the ground all whit with frost but a fine fair day, 3ᵈ a high
wind & dry. Cut doun the last of the Corn, & got in a good deal of
the first Cut doun – at Night a heavey Rain

4 & 5 dry & Suney with frost at Night 6 Cold & windy with
Showrs – 7 a great deal of Rain 8ᵈ a Brisk drying wind got in
some more Oats – a good deal of the Crop Cut doun & taken in –
by dilegence in watching every dry moment – 9 mostly dry with a
Brisk wind, but Rain all night 10 dry & wind got in the rest of oor
<u>Oats</u> ,

from this to the 15 Brisk wind – Suney, & only Some flying Showrs
– from that to the 20 the Same weather. Most of the Crop Cutt doun
& a great deal taken in 23ᵈ Still fine weather for getting in the rest of
the Crop

24ᵗʰ very Cold & a most Sever frost at Night 25 a great deal
Snow 26 & 27 a great deal more Snow, the frost so Strong that the
Sune makes no impression on the Snow – Meat Froz. 28ᵗʰ – 29 – 30ᵗʰ
most perceing Cold high wind with Showrs of Snow & intence Frost
– wind West 31ᵗʰ a heavey fall of Snow all Night – great wreaths and
Blowing with wind from the East which had befor been North West.

Novʳ 1ᵗʰ fresh with drizling Rain at Night a most heavey Rain
the 2ᵈ the Snow mostly gon here & a fine day 3ᵈ the Same The
Crop not all Cut doun in Many Places, & a good deal to take
in 4ᵗʰ Rain 5 Raind the whole day – 6 a Tempest of wind &
Rain the whole day Such as I have Seldom heard, in the midle

of which from one oclock to 6 in the Evening the Mercury rose 7 degrees –

The 7 a fine day Came to Abd from this to the 12th the same fine open dry weather – 13 Still fine weather

19 very Cold 20 a good deal of Snow & hail 21th 22 & 23d Cold & frost at Night, but the Snow gon & Seem to be little Lying on the Hills on the 20 a great deal Thunder heard in diffrent places & Lightning along with it.

from the 23 to the 8th most Changeable weather the one Day hard Frost next a dush of Rain. Some nights voilent Storm of wind & Rain – 11th Rain every day this day hail 12 Rain – from this to the 19 Rain & thick heavey Sky Every Day –

from this to the 22d the Same weather that day a Strong frost 23 the Same 24 Showrs of Snow 25 & 26 the Same Showrs of hail & Snow hard frost and very Cold – a good deal of Snow in the Country 29 the Same weather till this day we have a heavey fall of Snow 30 & 31 more Snow –

Janr 1786 the first day a great deal of Snow, the Storm very deep 2d & 3d a more intence Frost Meat Roots & Milk Froze hard 4th the Same, 5 Thawd a little 6 a Tempest of wind from the East, & Raind the whol day here, but all Snow in the Country, & no going from House to house –

1786 Janr

in the Country they have thought this Storm more Sever & the frost Stronger then it was at any time the two by past winters by the Storm of wind on the 6th many Ships has been lost on this Coast –

from the 6 to the 12th Rain fogg, & Closs warm Air Every day – this day Cold & Some Snow 13 14 the Same 15 Strong frost & more Snow which is now very deep 16 the Same – in England near London the Snow 10 feet deep, & the Thames froze over in Some places – Many more Ships Lost on that Cost by the Storm on the 6 then was on this Cost –

17 & 18 frost, 19th fresh 20th the Same a fine warm Suney day 21 a Loud wind & Rain the whole day, the Snow quit gon here –

from the 21th to the End of this Month fine open Blowing weather Some days as warm as Summer, all work going on Briskly in the Country the ground dry

the 1th Feby Some Showrs of Snow – 2d & 3d Rain – from that to the 7 open Blowing weather – 8 Snow – Showrs of Snow frost & fresh to the 12th when we had a Storm of Rain & wind the whole Day from this to the 20th open weather & little frost – from the 20 to the 28 Dark hevey Sky very Cold & frost with Slight Showrs of hail –

Sevral times throw this winter in England & in Flanders they have had dreadfull Storms of Thunder & Lightning with Snow on the Ground _____

7th of March the Same weather Continoud Seldom any Sune & Sever frost – to the North & in England they have deep Snow _____

11th the Same weather the frost so Sever as put Stop for Some time past to all work – this day in the afternoon we had a Showr of Snow the flakes So Large as few People has ever Seen – the Ground was Soon Coverd 12 Frost – the Same to the 15th 16 & 17 Snow & Slit – from this to the 25 Showrs of Rain & Cold wind 26 Sever frost wind & Snow 27 the Same – from this to the End dry Mild weather 1 April the Same weather – Many Places Some Oats Sowd

6 Still the Same weather hardly a Showr Sometimes frost in the Night – Some Oats Sowd – the Same weather to the 8 when we had some Showrs of Snow & Sever Frost, the 9 the Loch Froze hard –

10 Sever Frost & Loud wind – from this to the 14 Cold & dry 15 & 16 warmer

19th Still fine warm dry Weather the Oat Seed fare advanced Every way –

20th Came to Disblair the Larch begun to look Green Pear & Aple flowrish pritty well advanced, but not near Blown Spring flowrs all out Peas Sowd befor winter all just above Ground, & Peas Sowd in the Spring little Less Peas Sowd & Petatos Planted

from this to the 24 fine Suney days & dry, but Cold dwes or Frost at Night 25 A good deal Rain up the Country with Thunder – 26 very Cold & dry – not a drop Rain here the Same to the 30th when the Ground was Coverd with Snow, but was Soon Melted – Showrs of hail & Snow throw the Day –

1786 May

the Same the 1th Day of May – The Goosberrie Bushes & Curran in full Leaf & Flowrish Some Cherrie Plumb & Aple & Pear flowrish whit – a grate deal of Briar up & looking Green Every Body Bussie with there Bear Land –

from the first to the 4th Milder with fogg & Showrs of Rain the 4th a Storm of wind & Rain the whole day – 5th Cold & hazie 6 dry & Suney Strong frost at Night 7th the Same – from this to the 12 dry weather but very Cold – that day a deal of Rain & 13 a Storm of wind & Rain the whole day. from this to the 19 dry with high wind & always Some frost at Night the Larch in high Glory Some of the Young plain Leaves Expanded – the flowrish of the Wall Trees Almost fully Blown but non Yet opend on the Standerds. the Bear Seed fare advanced Every way Many People quit don <u>Oor Bear Seed</u> finishd the 20th & the Grass Seed Sowd & Rolld

from this to the 28 dry Blowing Suney weather Cold mostly & some little frost at Night –

the Grass very poor & people in great want to there Beasts

the Beach Tree & plain just out the Hathorn & Rane – the Birk is not much more then penny Brod yet – non of the Standerds but one Pear has the flowrish Blown. the Wall Trees & gine in full Blow, & Rich of flowrish Strawberries in flowrish a Sallett with Radish at Table.

from the 28 May to the 7th June Exceding warm weather not a drop Rain but Some dwe or fogg at Night all the Trees now in full glory the Laburnum in Blosum & the Rane all the Standard Fruit Trees – Strawberries & first Sown Peas in Bloum Even the Ash fully Expanded on most Trees.

10th Still the Same weather – great drught & Rain much wishd for 16 Still not a drop Rain & for some days past Cold as in Winter, & no Sune, the wind Exceding Sharp. the Hay Crop much hurt – a great deal of Fruit Set but all falling off – & every thing looking very Badly just now – frost often at Night

from the 16 to the 20 very warm Bright Sune shine little wind. no Rain but foggs at Night 23^d very foggy & Some Thunder at a distance but no Rain 24 wind & Bright Sun shine 25 Exceding hot & has been so Since the 16 a few Strawberries Rip – 26 This day a fine Mild Rain which has Continoud all fornoon, the first drop we have had Since the 13th May – Moon Changd at <u>11 oclock last Night.</u>

Jully 3^d Some drizling Showrs of Rain Every day Since the 26 June pritty high wind for most part – which day we had at Table Strawberries, Some Cherries & green Peas –

from the 3 of Jully to the 12 Exceding Cold & windy little Sune with Skifs of Rain here, but Snow in the Hills. the Crop all begining to Shute, but So Short much of it will hardly Cut – the Hay Crop very poor – what is here as good as Most, <u>& all in Tramp Colls.</u>

13th warm & Sun shine – the Bees Swarmd – 14th more Windy & Clouded Sky 15 & 16 hot & a good deal wind – we have had no Rain Since the 13 May that has gon the lest into the ground _____

Jully 1786

17 the Same & at Night So great a frost as to make a feald of Petatoes we Seed going by Kintor as Black as dulce 18 a fine warm day 19 in the Morning a good Showr of Rain but the ground quit dry

in a few Hours – 20 Skifs of Rain & Cold 21 Wind & Suney 22 oor Hay put in the Sow some Showrs in the afternoon – 23ᵈ a good deal of Rain –

from this to the 27 Showrs of Rain Every day. this day & the 28 heavy Rain wind, & Cold 29 the Same could not want a fire 30 Calm & the Air a little Milder 31 the Same –

from Augs 1ᵗʰ to the 9ᵗʰ modrat weather 10 & 11 thick Easterly fogg 12 & 13 a great deal Rain from the 13ᵗʰ to the 16 foggy drizling weather 17 the Same & Still Cold 20 Still the Same weather.

the Gin Trees in the garden & wood Loaded with Fruit but all Burst & spoild with the Rain - a great deal Goosberries & all kinds smal Fruits Plenty of Aples but Smal few Pears this year

21 Most heavey Rain the whole day but the fogg gon 22 more Rain 23 Showrs of Rain & Frost at Night very Strong 24 the Same 25 a Clear fair day 26 the Same but Frost at Night 27 Raind most of the day 28 & 29 heavey Showrs of Rain Some Bear Cut & a good deal would be Cut if dry weather

30 & 31 a most Voilent Storm of wind has hurt the Bear Crop a little Thrown doun most of the Standerd Fruit

---

the 11 of this Month an Earthquake was felt in Several parts of the South of Scotland & North of England but did no hurt or damage.

---

few days this Month we Could want Fire & most of it Frost at Night

Septʳ 1ᵗʰ this day Showrs of Rain & as Cold as winter & high wind, 2ᵈ the Same with rain 3ᵈ & 4 pritty fair 5 the Same – but a great frost at night Ice on the pools 6 a fine day Cut doun oor Bear – a good deal Bear Cut doun every way & some fealds of Early Oats – 7 Rain & very Cold – 8ᵗʰ a Storm of wind & Showrs.

The 9 Showrs & frost at Night – the Same to the 12ᵗʰ 13 pritty fair 14ᵗʰ & 15 Rain & wind the whol day – 16 fair in the fornoon & Suney Cut doun feald peas Rain at Night 17 a fine Brisk wind & fair all Day 18 Calm & Suney & a great frost at Night Oor Bear taken in.

19 a fine Day & a good deal of wind a great deal of Bear taken in & Early Oats – little of oor own kind of Oats Cut doun –

from this to the 22ᵈ fine dry weather – begun to Cut Some Oats but most of it not ready 23 a fine Day 24 hazie & thick Air. from this to the End of the Month fair with very high wind & frost great deal Cut doun – wher Rip, but much of the Crop not ready for Cutting

14 & 15 this Month in Many parts of England a hurricane of wind throw doun Some Houses & overturnd Severl Stage Coaches & Waggons – Several People Killd & many hurt & much Loss at Sea. _____

1786

Octr 1 th a fine day at Night a heavey Rain 2^d Closs & as warm as in June 3^d a thick Air & wind Cut doun more Oats, but non got in yet. 4 a Vast deal of Rain the whole day – 5 the Same 6 the Same – 7 a fair Day 8th most heavy Rain & wind – The Watter Don over all the Haughs & the Burn like a River – 9 fair & a good deal of wind put up a Smal Stack of the first Cut Oats – the dryest part of Som Stuaks –

10 thick Air & drizling Rain 11th the Air more Clear with Showrs 12th wind with heavy Showrs of Snow & Sever frost at Night – 13 & 14 the Same – the Hills Coverd with Snow – it lys here every way where the Sune dos not Shine a great deal of the Crop to Cut doun & a great deal in Stuck which is quit wait into the Heart – <u>the Meal in the Market giveing 14 pence the Peck</u>

15 a fair dry Day but Cloudy Sky – 16 the Same Cut doun the Last of oor Corns – & got in a Smal Stack 17 dry – took in a little more Corn – frost at Night 18 a warm Suney Day 19 & 20 dry but no wind 21 thick fogg to the Door 22 quit Calm fogg in the Morning Sunny the rest of the Day - always frost at Night –

from this to the 28 dry but Calm with foggs often & frost at Night – that day a good Brisk wind got in the Last of oor <u>Corns</u> a great deal Cut doun & got in, but Still a great deal to do in many Places – 29 fair Calm & frost with heavey Sky 30 & 31 thick drizling hazey wether

Novr 1 & 2 the Same 3^d a good deal Rain 4 & 5 Showrs Calm & frost at Night – from this to the 8 fair & Calm with Frost at Night – <u>Came to Abd</u>

12th the Same weather Continoud from the 12 to the 17 dry Blowing weather which has Brought in all the Crop Except Some little in Very late Places this day 17 hail & Rain – Snow in the Hills –

from this to the 23th Voilent Storms of wind with Showrs of Rain, but Snow in the Hills, & Some parts of the Low Country 24 25 & 26 Rain Constant – with Loud wind the 26 – 27th pritty fair – Drizling Rain to the End of the Month

1 Decr Rain 2 fair 3 a Storm of Rain & wind from this to the

12 much the Same weather few days fair & Voilent Storms of wind & Rain –

The Same to the 14, when we had Frost 15 Frost & Showrs of Snow – The Same every Day to the 21 – Frost with very little Snow on the Ground till the 28 when it Thawd 29 Rain – 30 & 31 frost

Jan.r 1787

the 1th 2 & 3d – from that to the 12 Mild weather 14 the Same weather

24 Still the Same weather Some Nights a little Frost with fine Suney warm Days 26 Still the Same weather little frost & warm days 27 this day Cold & Showrs of Hail & Snow 28 more Snow 29 high wind with Rain from this to the 7 Feb.r fresh open weather Sometimes a little Frost at Night & then Showrs of Rain & very warm

---

Corn & fother giveing 25 Sh the Boll - Bear 26 Shillings Some Oats Sowd at Towie End of Last Month & Some Sowd now near Abd.

Feb.r 1787

10 Feb.r Still the Same weather 11 Rain & Blowing 12 the Same 13 very high Wind 14 Frost 15 the Hills Coverd with Snow 16 & 17 Cold & Showrs of Rain

---

Some Corn & fother Sold this week at 30 Shillings the Boll

---

from this fine Mild dry weather till the 24 that day heavey Rain – all the Spring Flowers in full Blow Goosberries & Currans the Leave near Expanded & flowrish buds on the Trees far advanced – Many People Sowing near Abd non of the Flowrish at Kemnay Expanded the 8 of March & very little Sowed

fine warm weather to the End of this Month –

March 2d a Voilent Storm of wind from the West 3 a Storm of wind & Rain from the East, this Rain Snow in the Hills, 4th Showrs of Snow & Cold – from this to the 9 Cold & high wind, Showrs of Rain & Snow in the Hills. the Same weather Cold & high winds & frost at night to the 13 –

from that Milder weather to the 17th Every body Sowing now this Day Oat Seed begun at Disblair 22 Still dry weather warm Air, & often high wind Every thing made great Progress Since the 13 – Seed

Some Apple Blosom the hathorn pritty green Currans & goosberries quit green & in Blosom – from this to the 29 the Air mild tho a little Frost Some Nights & Showrs of Rain after it. _____

The Cherry Plumb at Kemnay in full Blosom the other Fruit Trees fare advanced & Larch pretty Green – Oat Seed Except in Low wate Ground mostly don Every way _____

30 & 31 very Cold & a great deal of Rain Snow in the Hills

April 1 2 3 Cold air but pritty dry 4 the Same heavey Sky Clear dry weather to the 9 – 10 & 11th the Same 12 very Cold

Came out to Disblair 13 wind & Showrs of Snow & Frost for Several Nights past 14 & 15 Milder Air

Goosberries & Currans in Leaf & flowrish Some Pear & Cherry flowrish quit Blown – Some Plain Trees the Leaf Expanded – the Birch hardly any Buds Green – the Larch Green & the Young Trees full of Cons – all the Spring flowrs in great Glory –

the Grass fare advanced, but much hurt by the late frost & Cold weather – Every body in distress for Meat to there Beasts – the last Crop so Scrimp & Short that but for the mild winter many of the Cattle would have dyed. The Meal giveing 14 pence the peck in the Market.

from the 15 to the 20 Exceding Cold frost at Night Loud wind & Showrs of Rain or Snow 21 Still the Same Colder then any day we had in winter & the Frost in Some places So Sever as to be on the pools at 11 oclock forenoon.

22 & 23 Showrs of Rain & no Frost but Still Cold 24 Frost 25 a good deal of Rain 26 Cold & windy

We can See little hurt the frost has don here the Briar & grass looks well & every thing in the Garden Tho little advanced Since we Came here – 27 heavey & Constant Rain the whole day

28th & 29th a Tempest of wind with Frost & Showrs of Snow 30 the Same & bitter Cold

May 1787

the 1 of May the Ground all Coverd with Snow – all the Rain we have had Snow further up the Country & hills deep of Snow – 2d a mild Air & Calm –

This Storm & long Cold weather has taken off all the out feald Grass – The last Crop So Short & Provendor So Scarce that but for the open fine mild winter Peoples Cattle would have dyed & now they have nothing to give them – What hay can be Spaird here is Selling out in Stons to those in more want. The Meal at 14 pence the peck

from the 2d May to the 7th the weather Milder & little frost this Day begun Bear Seed the Plain Tree mostly in full Leaf – Plumbs & Pears in full Flurish Some Blown flurish on the Gins – & a Standard Pear Tree the Birch not penny Broad yet –

8 a fine Mild Day 9 Cold & Some Showrs of hail 10 much the Same 11th Some Rain & a thick fogg. 12 from 2 in the morning to 6 we had a Voilent Storm of Thunder, with Rain but not heavey here, but up to the west most Voilent Speat of Rain – The Watter Don over flowd all the haughs Swept of Seed & Earth & has don vast hurt.

13th Cold with driziling Rain most of the Day & frost at Night 14th 15 & 16 dry with high wind bitter Cold & frost at Night

We can now Say the Birch is penny broad & all the Trees the Leaf expanded except the Oak & Ash Strawberries in full Flowrish & the Currans & goosberries Knotted. Radish often at Table – the <u>Bear Seed finishd</u> – Cherries as Big as Smal Peas Damsons & Gins all whit over_____

21 Still the Same weather Every thing here Seemd little hurt by the Severity of the weather till the Thunder Storm – Now Every thing is Broun & weatherd like & great Complaint on the Corn not Comming well up & what is going off again.

22 It Thunderd from 10 oclock fornoon till 6 in the afternoon but not one drop of Rain here tho in diffrent places the had the Ground Coverd with hail like Flakes of Ice

23 & 24 dry Cloudy Sky, high wind & frost at night 25 Some Showrs of Rain

from that to the 1 June Still exceding Cold & Blowing with sometimes a Showr of Rain or Hail & frost at night 2 & 3d the Same 4 a good deal of Rain – the Rane Tree & the Lauburnum & Hawthorn now in full Blow & the Ash Leaf pritty well out the Standerd Trees in full Flowrish a good deal of Blosom on the Peas. French Beans well advancd_____

The 5 June a Storm of wind & Rain till about 8 in the Evening when we had a fall of Snow. the Ground all Coverd & Continowd So all Night

the 6th in the Morning it was Still whit & froze as hard as if in winter & where the Sun did not Shine was hard at 12 oclock

7th Some Rain & the 8 Rain & high wind the Air Still as Cold, & frost at Night. The 9 the Air Milder & no frost 10th Same all day but frost at Night_____

Everything Excedingly hurt the French Beans quit taken off, & all Petatos above Ground the Larch quit Broun & the young Shoots of many of the Spruce Firs the Leaf of the Ash now pritty fare advancd all like Dulce.

June 1787

11 & 12th fine warm Sunny days – 13 14 & 15th Cold Air & frost at Night. no Rain to take of the Bad Efects of the frost 16 the Same 17 Some Showrs but Still Cold 18 a great deal of Rain.

from this to the 23 Rain Every day & no Frost & the Air Milder 24 a fine day – 25 It Raind most heavely the whole day 26 Showrs of Rain 27 a great deal of Rain

Gosberrie Pye – & young Turnep at Table –

28 & 29 dry & pritty warm, but Some Frost at Night - 30 a fine Mild day

Jully 1th a thick fogg all day 2 & 3 warm & Suney begun to Cut Hay a fine Crop 4 the Same – 5 the Same fine warm days oor Bees Swarmd & this the first day we Could be intirly withoot fire tasted Strawberries & Cherries a few Green Peas Could be got

6 warm & fine 7 Rain & Some Thunder the Air much Colder & Some frost at night 8 Rain & frost at Night 9 Cold with Showrs – Some of the Hay in Colls, but mostly as Cut 10 & 11 fair but very Cold got all the Hay in pritty Large Colls

from this to the 17 Showr Every day with very little Sune & frost often at Nigh & Exceding Cold The Crop in good ground looking well & a good deal of Bear Shot but the out fealds & Low ground very poorly

18 dry & Some of the Hay got into the Yard 19 havey Rain the Air a little warmer 20 dry – Green Peas at Table – Cherries & Strawberries for the Second time – a Second Swarm of Bees this day – the 21 the Air very like more Rain 22 a fine day – got another Swarm Bees – 23d got all the Hay into the Corn Yard,

24 fair 25 a heavey Rain in the Morning 26 & 27 dry 28 Rain in the afternoon & all night & Continowd to Rain 29 all day Rain

from this to the Second of August pritty dry that day a Hurrican of wind & Rain – hurt & destroyd Every thing in the Garden 3 a good deal of wind – from this to the 10 fine dry warm days the only Summer day we have had –

betwixt the 10 & Eleven a great deal of thunder & Lightning Especialy at Sea but no Rain 11 dry but Colder that day got oor Hay put in the Stack or Sow – 13 Cold & Showrs of Rain

the Crop greatly better Since this Month begun & Every body thinks it a fine Crop it is now all Shot & the Bear filling well Petatos at Market at 10 pence the Peck

14 thick Air & Showrs of Rain from this to the 18 Rain Every day & thick fogg that day the Air Clearer

from this to the 24 Changable weather Som days Warm but mostly Cold with Showrs & frost at night, very little of the Bear begun to Chang Colour – Bear Sold on the Ground at 20 Sh the Boll.

Oat Meal giveing 1 Sh & 13 pence the peck

from this to the 25 Rain & foggy Cold weather, often Frost at Night the Same to the 29 – that & the 30 & 31 Mild & warm Air

from this to the 5 Septr warm weather Some days very hot great dwes & foggy at Night –

Eat new Bear Meal a good deal of Bear Cut near Abd & where it was Early Sowd. Petatoes Selling at 8 pence the peck

10 the Same weather but a great Frost last Night Every body Cutting doun Some Bear –

13 Still the Same warm dry weather no Rain Since 25 last Month

Sept 1787

14 Colder 15th and 16 Rain & wind & very Cold <u>17 the Same & the Mercury So Low as almost out of Sight</u> – frost at night 18 Clear & Sunny frost at night 19 the Same 20 Some Showrs 21 a Voilent Storm of wind & Rain at night – Lightning & distant Thunder along with it – 22 wind & Rain 23^d a good deal of wind but fair 24th the Same & Cold 25 the Same

The Crop thought fine Every way, if got Safely in – A good deal of the Bear Crop is So – & Some new Oat Meal in the Abd Market – but very little Cut doun of Oats hear about – & much of it very green yet.

26 a fine day 27 Cold windy & Skifs of Showrs – Begun to Cut <u>Corn</u> – Oor Bear this Year all Sold on the Ground.

fine weather till the 2 Oct^r – Most of the Bear Cut doun every way & a great deal in, but little Oats Cut except in very Early places & a great deal Still green Oor Petatoes taken up a good Crop of them Every way –

from the 2^d to the 7 hazye thick weather & Showrs of Rain – very little work don – the 6 at Night the Air or Sky made a remarkable apperance with the Auroabole Red as Fire –

8 & 9 fine days - Hazye & Rain the whol day at Night a Storm of most Voilent wind & Rain which Continoud the 11 Most of the Day, 12 Rain & wind.

This Storm Beat all the Strong Corns flat to the Ground as if a Roller had been drawn over it –

13 pritty fair, & the Air warmer - at Night the Sky full of the Auro— Red as Blood, then like Fire

14 a fine day like Summer 15 fair Calm & heavey Sky 16 Rain 17 Showrs of Rain

17 fair Cut doun the last of oor <u>Oats</u> – Every body Cutting doun
but non Can be taken in - 18 more <u>Rain</u> 19 & 20 Showrs of Rain 21
fine day. hoped on the 22 to have got much taken in but the Rain
Came on at Night & a good deal throw that day 23 fair

24 got in a good deal – Every body Leading – 25 fair with
the Strongest frost at night the Ice was on the pools at Mid day –

26 Showrs of Rain from that to the 31th Constant Drizling
Rain, Calm & thick fogg –

A great deal Corn in Stuck & much to Cut doun & what is
in the Yard not keeping –

from this to the 4 Sept (*Novr*) Rain Every day that day the 4
Septr (*Novr*) Constant heavy Rain – A great deal of the Crop must
be Lost –

5 a dry windy day got in the last of oor Corns 6th & 7 fair a
great deal Cut doun & taken in but Still much to do that night a
Sever Frost - Rain the 8th 9 a Tempest of wind & Rain the whole
day 10 Still wind & heavey Sky – 11 Rain 12 more Rain

13 pritty fair 14 Snow in the Morning the Ground all Whit
Came to Abd _____

a great deal Still to Cut doun & to take in – 14 more Snow from
this to the 21 Showrs 22 fair & frost 23 Some Showrs of Snow windy
& very Cold

from this to the End of the Month frost in the Night & fine
fair Suney days

Decr 1787

Decr 1th the Same <u>The Crop all got in now.</u> 2d Rain the most
of the day 3d & 4th thick Drizling Days.

from this to <u>the 9 Strong frost but this</u> day it powrd out Rain
without intirmition & in all the South of Scotland there was Such
floods of Rain Snow thundr & Lightning as has not been rememberd

this floods has also been in England & Irland the Rivers carring
Houses Cattle & every thing in ther way & Severl Lives Lost _____

10 heavey & Showrs 11 Rain the whole day 12 Showrs of Rain 13
& 14 Strong Frost 15 & 16 Showrs & Sleet 17 Frost 18 heavey Rain
the whole day 19 the Same 20 drizling Rain 21 a Strong Frost 22 the
Same with Some Showrs of Snow 23 frost 24 a great fall of Snow 25
more Snow 26 Showrs of Snow & great frost

To the 29 Sever Frost & Clear Suney days 30 Milder 31 Thaw
with Cold wind from the South.

1788 Janr 1h the Snow mostly gon 2d heave Sky & drizling Rain the

whole day the Night time Thunder the 3ᵈ warm like Summer Rain at
Night – 4 the Same

This little Storm here was most Sever in England the Snow 10 feet
deep in many Places & Several Ships froze in -in the River Thames

---

5 & 6 Strong frost 7 & 8 Rain from this to the 12 frost & fresh by
turns that Night a good fall of Snow 13 More Snow & Sever frost 14
frost 15 fresh 16 much of the Snow gon a good brisk wind & fresh –

from the 16 to the 22 open weather with wind & Showrs of Rain –
23ᵈ frost & a good fall of Snow 24 frost in the morning then Thaw &
all the Snow gon Eer Night 25 Wind & Showrs of Rain 26 very high
wind with Showrs of Snow

from this to the 3ᵈ Febʳ Some days fresh with Smal Showrs of
Rain & others Sever Frost – from this to the 9 open weather with
often Rain. the Ground always So Wat that very little Labouring has
been got don

10 frost 11 Some Snow & frost from that to the 13 open weather
14 15 16 Constant Rain 17 Rain 18 Snow 19 Sever Frost 20 Snow to
the 25 Showrs of Snow, frost, & thaw, & frost again.

this Snow not deep Even in the Hills & very little here 28 frost
& Showrs of Snow Every day Since the 25 & a good deal of Snow
in the Country no Plughs going Since the 18 of this Month –

29ᵗʰ & March 1ᵗʰ thick heavey Sky with drizling Rain 2ᵈ & 3ᵈ
the Same 4ᵗʰ Showrs of Snow throw the whole day, & at Night a
more Sever Frost then we have had all winter, 5 more Snow –

6ᵗʰ Strong frost, high wind & Snow all night, Such Drift &
Blowing that they Computed a foot & half Snow fully.

The 7 traveling from many Places was Stopt all Doors & windows
here Blown up, 8 wind & most Sever frost 9 Calm & Suney Some
Snow in the Night & the frost as Strong as Ever 10 & 11 the Same
but windy –

to the 15 Still Strong frost & Exceding Cold non of the Snow
gon but what the Sune & Lenth of the day takes away.

March 1788

16 a new fall of Snow wind & Exceding Cold – from this to the 20
frost & Cold – that day Rain & Slite the whol Day. 21 Milder Air
but the Snow Still lying where drifts was.

22 the Same no work has been don in the Country all this time in
the fealds or Gardens – 31 Every day since the 22 heavey thick drizling
weather & Some Rain Every day, no work don, or any Seed Sown.

April 1th a dry Day, & Some wind & Drought – the fare Hills Still Coverd with Snow 2d Rain the whol day 3d Voilent Rain till mid day then Snow 4 Snow the whol day 5 Some Showrs of Snow & very Cold

from this the 13th fine dry warm days a great deal of work don, that day & the 14 high wind & Some Ramping Showrs – 15 the Same Showrs of Snow & Hail.

16 milder Came oot to Disblair. found Oat Seed begun here 14 & a good deal don all Round Very little Vigetation here Greens & Plants in the Garden all taken off - the Goosberries pritty green & the Flowrish Buds on the Trees begining to Swel Spring flowrs in Blosom The Larch takeing a green Cast –

from this to the 27 Rough Blowing weather Showrs of Rain & Hail, but nothing to Stop the work for a Moment Every body Bussie to get the Seed in the Ground. That Day oor Oat Seed finishd Some Pear & Cherrie Blosom Expanded – The Grass looking very Green

29 begun Bear Seed the Leaf of the young Plain Tree Expanded 30 & 31 the Same weather the Briar apearing in all the first Sown ground.

May 1th Mild & warm & some Rain – from this to the 8 dry weather & several Nights a good Strong frost – that day Rain the 9 more Rain _____

the Bear was Sown the 29 April was all Green the 4 May _____ Strawberries in flowrish the Larch in high Glory

10 Rain & hail & high wind Exceding Cold 11 Snow & hail & high wind, frost at Night. the Bear Briar that Came up So quickly all taken off, & Many things hurt in the Garden –

from this to the 16 dry Blowing Cold weather & often frost at Night – the Birch now what may be Calld penny Broad. the Plain Hathorn & many other Trees in Leaf 17 – 18 – 19 Milder Air & hot Sun with fogg at night – Some Cherries Set Radish at Table Strawberries in full Flowrish Aples Gin Pears & Plumb all in full Blow Except the Standerd Aples

20 a Smal Showr & mild warm air 21 warm 22d another Showr & warm Bear Seed finishd

from the 22 to the 29 hot as Jully – oor fire off the whole day Cherries as big as Gins Currans & Goosberries very forward Peas in full Blosom – the Rane & Laburnum in Flowr – the young Ash the Leaf Expanded – Pears & apples Set –

28 & 29 Cold & windy with Some Slight Showrs of hail 30 Still Cold Air – No Rain that Could weat the Surface of the ground Since the 9th – Goosberries Large Enoch for Tarts –

June 1788

from this to 2ᵈ June Still dry weather. that day Some Smal Soft Showrs of Rain. Sallad at Table – from this to the 12ᵗʰ dry Hot Sunshine all day & for Most part frost at Night Some time the Ground whit Early in the morning – not a drop of Rain – Spinage at Table – very little Fruit Sett the Hay Excedingly Short & all Shot – in Some places dryd & Yellow, & Obliged to be Cut doun – the Hory dew has Spoild the foilige of all the plains – Bick &c has atackd the Birck this year – & Trees never Seed it on befor – <u>Green goosberries at Table</u> – the Fruit not Swiling & droping off –

The 18 Still the Same Weather Hot Sun – the Air for most part Sharp with wind & frost 17 & 18 very warm & no frost Some fogg Morning & Night & this day a Smal Showr hardy to be perceved

19 the Air Colder with wind & Rain most of the day & in some places Snow 20 a fine warm dry day – Every thing looking much refreshd – Bees Swarmd – dry to the 24 That day it Raind the whol day & Night – <u>Green Peas</u> Ready Some Rip Strawberries & Cherries

from this to the 28 dry & warm – That day Cold & a drizling Rain all day – 29 much the Same – 30 dry a <u>Second Swarm Bees</u>

1 Jully dry – The Hay greatly Mended – & the Fruit Sweling, & Every thing much recoverd by the Rain Peas now in plenty & Artichock at Table 2 & 3 fine days but at nigh of the 3ᵈ a great deal Lightning & Thunder at a distance with some Rain

The 4 Jully most haevey Rain all the forenoon 5 a fine dry Day – begun to Cut <u>Hay</u> 6 fair the park Cut oot 7ᵗʰ put in Colls – from this to the 13 Rain Every day & last night Distand Thunder 14 a high wind a great deal Thunder at a distance & no Lightning – at night heavey Rain – befor it Came the <u>Hay</u> got into the Yard in Large Tramp Colls – 15 & 16 More Rain 17ᵗʰ in the fornoon Rain for a little like a Watter Spout Much Thundan at a distance no Lightning & Continoud Rain most of the Day

18 more Rain 19 Constant Rain the whole day 20 & 21 Showrs but begun to Cut the Hay that was kept for Seed & this day & the 22 & 23 Exceding Hot & dry 24 Showrs 25 the Same 26 dry in the forenoon got the Hay Threshd & in to the Yard afternoon Rain & not so warm this two days –

from this to the End of the Month warm & Showrs but Some times like frost in the Night _____

from the 12 to the 17 of this Month Voilent Storms of Hail, Thunder

& Lightning & in Some places like little Shocks of Earthquakes in many Places of Britan & in France.

1 August & Second dry fine warm days, the Crop looking well Every way 3ᵈ Exceding Hot – 4 the Same The Hay put in a Sow____
5 the Same Exceding Hott - The 8 Seed Petatos at Table as Large they will be in winter - Still dry hot weather 9 the Same –
Bear Sold on the ground – begining to Change Colour – at 17 Sh the Boll, & Oats at 17/6 _____
10 & 11 the Same weather Some Bear Cut at Kintor _____

August 1788

from this to the 15 hot weather with hasty Showrs the 16 havery Rain & to the South Exceding heavey Rain with Thunder & Lightning Bear Meal in the Market
from the 16 to the 21 little Rain & fine warm weather the Bear Chainging Colour Every way, & Cutting doun in Early places – A great deal of Smal fruit Obliged to Sell Some Goosberries at 10 pence the peck –
23 Wind with Some Rain Bear begun to be Cut here – 24ᵗʰ windy from this to the End of the Month fine warm weather with Mild Showrs now & then – Every body Cutting doun Some Bear, & all the Crop Ripning & Comming on Quickly –
Septr 1 & 2ᵈ the Same weather from this to the 8 th Still warm weather rather more Rain & thick fogg Mostly at Night 8 & 9 Exceding hot with fogg at Night & morning, Every Body now Cutting doun Bear & Early Oats - the Early Aples & Pears all Rip & Pulld
10 Rain in the morning but a fine day 11ᵗʰ & 12 dry & rather Colder with wind 13 Rain 14 fair but Cold 15 the Same with wind pritty high – 16ᵗʰ Loud wind with drizling Rain morning & heavy Rain the rest of the day –
from this to the 20 only Some Showrs a great deal Cut doun & a good deal taken in – all the Bear Sold & keept taken into the Yard this day 21 a great deal Rain & windy & Cold 22 thick & Some Rain 23 24 25 fine dry Suney Blowing days Many of the little tennants don Shearing & mostly in –
That night & most of the 26 a Tempest of Wind, but the day being Cloudy not much harm don 27ᵗʰ don with oor Hervest 28 dry & 29 all in the Yard – 30 & 31ᵗʰ Still dry & windy –
Octr 1 ᵗʰ 2 & 3ᵈ Still dry. this morning a Stronger frost then we have had very little round this to Cut doun or take in – 4ᵗʰ A Voilent Storm of wind 5 Windy –

from this to the 13 fine dry Suney days with Some little frost at Night, not a drop Rain Since 22 Septr _____

a fine Crop of Petatos – Some Wighting a pound Except 4 ounce, & the Turnip Large & fine – 14 & 15 the same fine warm Suney days 16 Rain 17 a Storm of wind 18 & 19 fair with frost

20 Some Showrs & very Cold the Same weather to the 24 – that night a Meteor or Some firey Apearance in the Air 25 & 26 the Same weather Cold windy & Some Showrs with Some Snow in the Hills

from this to the End of the Month fine dry weather & Mild Aire the long Continouance of Drought has almost Laid the Mills & hardly any watter for Beasts the Springs mostly dry a very uncommon thing, this time of the Year.

Came to Abd the 30 Octr The Day & Roads like Midle of Summer 31th the Same

Novr 1 Windy & at Night a Voilent Storm of Wind which Continoued most of the 2^d with a good deal of Rain, 3^d Rain but no heavey Rain 4 dry & at Night the highest wind I have heard with Lightning - 5 & 6 dry & Mild Air 7th Rain & Wind 8 the Same 9 & 10th Mild Air with wind – no frost all this Month – 11 the Same 12 a great deal of Rain 13 Showrs of Snow Cold & frost at night 14 the Same 15 more Snow very Cold 16 Rain 17 Cold with wind & Showrs of Rain –

Novr 1788

from this to the 25 Mild fine weather. the Grass & every thing as Green as in Summer from that to the End of the Month thick heavey weather with Showrs off & on

1 Decr the Same & no frost till the 8th which a fine day with a little frost 9 the Pools froze the first Ice we have Seen this Autom 10 frost & Snow in the Hills 11 frost with a good deal of Snow 12 more Snow all coverd with Snow 13 & 14 Sever frost – perceing Cold & Showrs of Snow, 15th a heavey fall of Snow – this Snow Lay with Strong frost & Showrs of Snow till the 18 when it Thawd a little & Some Snow falling of the Houses –

19 20 & 21th the Same – 22 a new fall of Snow 23 frost 24 Thaw & a great deal of the Snow gon 25 the Same – 27 a heavey fall of Snow & Sever frost 28 the Same 29 Thaw or Soft Air. 30 th & 31 the Same & a good deal of the Snow gon.

1789 Jan^ry 1th a Strong Frost 2^d the Same from that to the 8th Soft Mild Air with Rain almost Every day – the Mercury Exceding high – & the Snow greatly gon – 9 the Same – 10 Snow & very Cold 11 more Snow & intence frost 12th the Same Every thing in most houses frezing – 13 Snow with high wind & Strong frost –

14 Exceding Cold – fresh and frost by turns – 15 Thaw with Showrs of Rain 16 Frost & very Cold _____

traveling almost put a Stop to, & little of the thawes we have had in the Country – the frost & Storm here is nothing to what they have had in France, Germany &c – & Even in England where there has not been Such Frost or So Sever a Winter known the thermometer at Lipsick the 17 Decr was 27 degrees below what it was in 1709, 1740 or 1782 – the Rhine Froze So as wagons & Cariges passed over – the River Theams Froze in Many Places with Booths & Shops on it ____

17 Rain the whole day 18 Rain afternoon – 19 Sever frost & a good deal of Snow 20 high wind at West & Sever frost 21 Mild Air 22 the Snow Melting – 23d frost & More Snow 24 & 25 Rain

from this to the 31th Blowing Cold Gloomy weather with Showrs of Rain

Febr 1th a fine warm day the 2d as much So as Summer open Blowing weather to the 7th & all the Snow in the Hills gon -

the Same weather Continoud till the 11 when we had Several Showrs of Snow & very Cold 12 frost – from this to the 16 open weather – that day a good deal of Snow 17th Rain & wind 18 a fine Mild day –

from this to the 3 March open weather a great deal of Rain & Cold but hardly any frost till last Night a great frost – hard where the Sune has not been at 3 oclock

from this to the 8 Showrs of Snow with frost at Night & Sometimes Rain – this day a hard frost & Snow in the hills

9th a great fall of Snow & Blowing 10 Snow most of the Day, Calm 11 More Snow & Blowing 12th a foot depth of more Snow Calm since last night – Calm but Still Continous to Snow - A great Storm in England Came on Sooner then here 13 more Snow wind & frost 14 Still more Snow & So deep to the South that this day the Post was obliged to return –

March 1789

15 & 16 Still more Snow & no Melting in the hight of the day the Post that Should have Come on Saturday Came only on Sunday & the Sundays Post on Monday The Mial Carred by two Men & the North Post the Same –

17th & 18 Still Showrs of Snow – No Such Storm is rememberd here – in Many places drifts of Snow 15 foot high – an openin Made to the South for the Fly & Post – 30 Men & the Country People imployd to Cast the Snow to Stonhive Still no Hors Can go the Lenth of Disblair

the 19 Still Showrs of Snow & frost 20 & 21 a kind of thaw & the Road more passable but at night a great frost 22 Snow again 23 a Strong Frost 24 the Same 25 Early in the morning a heavey fall of Snow 3 Inch deep on the Street at 11 oclock 26 Strong frost – from this to the 30 frost & Showrs of Snow 31 a good fall of Snow –

the Old Snow Still lys in the Country & is at Disblair as high as the Dycks – no thaw has been that has had any Efect in Melting the Snow in the Country path is made & Cast So as get Carriges to go on the high road – this Storm & great Snow is parshal – at Abd & 12 Milles round – after that the Snow not So deep & in many places up the Country no Snow at all – in Stradoun & in Morow they are Sowing in England tis the Same Some Countys Burried in Snow & Some no Snow at all _____

Meal at 9 pence the peck & the fother not Scarce as yet

April 1789 Abd

the 1th 2d & 3d the Same weather frost & Showrs of Snow the lest freshness has never been Since 21th of last month & then very little – The Sune Melts the Showrs as they fall but the Old Snow lys Even here

4 this day as thick & heavey a fall of Snow as We have Seen Continoud without the lest intermition from 7 in the morning till 12 mid day

5th 6 & 7 dry Cold & winday from this to the 12 Milder Air – dry frost at Night the Same weather Continoud to the 16 – the Snow gon Every where that the Sune & wind gets at – where there has been great drifts of Snow its Still unmelted - Every body is Sowing now

to the 16 the Same weather that day Rain 17 Rain & Cold from this to the 22d dry

Came out to Disblair that day a fine Mild Day – Rain in the Evening – begun Oat Seed there 13th & now Mostly over. Every thing looking very Blick the Larch just begining to Look Green Curran on the Wall in Flowrish & the Flowrish of Some Plumbs to look Whit Goosberries in Leaf –

23 Cold & Showrs of hail 24 very Cold & windy 25 Showrs & windy 26 a great deal of Rain 27 Rain Came on in the Evening & powrd oot at night & Continoud with little intermition all the 28

29 Showrs & Sunshin Still very Cold & frost at Night 30th dry day May 1th very Cold 2 begun Bear Seed very Cold & Showrs 3d Cold as winter Showrs of hail & Rain a good deal of Snow up the Country 4 Exceding Cold 5 in the morning the Ground whit with Snow –

May 1789

from this to the 15 Milder Air Loud Wind often & frequant Showrs of Rain. the Bear Seed fare advanced don here & in Several places the Plain Tree & Hors Chesnut the Leaf expanded – the Birch penny Broad – Pears Plumb &c in full Blow –

16 & 17 Mild Air with Showrs 18 & 19 high wind & Cold 20 & 21 the Same 22ᵈ thick fogg 23 a great deal of Rain & very Cold

24 fair & fogg at night 25 windy & fogg at night 26 a fine Suney Day 27 & 28 warm with drizling Showrs & fogg night & morning from this to the 31ᵗʰ foggy Weather – that day a vast deal of Rain

June 1ᵗʰ More Rain – all the Trees now – Except the Ash – in full foilage – Gins & Plumbs of all kinds whit over - the Strawberrie flowrishd Pears Sett Goosberries & Currans

from this to the 5ᵗʰ Rain Every Day & not So warm as want a fire any part of the day all this Season 6 the Same 7 Bitter Cold with Hail & Rain – 8 Showrs of Rain 9 a fair day & the Air more mild 10 the same 11 Cold & Rain in the Morning 12ᵗʰ fogg most of the day

from this to the 18 fine warm Sune the hight of the Day & fogg at Night & Morning – 19 The Same 20 rain in the Morning 21 thick fogg Most of the day, & very Cold. 22 Drizling Rain & fogg 23ᵈ Rain & Cold, 24 the Same & Cold as winter

Some Peas in Blosom – little apeerence of any fruit Sett tho the Trees was all Loaded with Blosom –

from the 24 to the End Cold & drizling Showrs & fogg nothing in the Garden Made any Progres this 10 days past

Jully 1ᵗʰ the Air a little Milder but heavey & Showrs – from this to the 6 Constant foggs Cold – the Wind Constantly North or South East this two Months hardly a day out of the East altogether – the fruit Trees as if Burnt, & the foilage of all the Trees much hurt – the Grass & Crop looking pritty well

begun to Cut Hay the 4ᵗʰ 6 & 7 Clear the hight of the day but thick fogg Morn & Night 8 a frost whit on the Grass Early this Morning

from this to the 15 Rain Every day – That day heavey Rain with Some Thunder Eat a Cherrie Strawberrie & a whap or two Green peas from Straloch the 13 _____

16 Eat the Same here – That day a great deal More Rain & distant Thunder 17 more Rain & Thunder at a Distance 18 more Rain & thunder

The Hay all Cut doun but in a Sad State here and Every where,

& a great Crop there is – 19 only Some Showrs the 20 the Same but more wind & got Some of the Hay in Smal Cocks – 21th the first fair day from End to End – & no fogg Since the <u>20 of June</u> –

22^d fair but Cold & heavey Sky – 23^d very Cold & drizling Rain 24 a fine fair day – 25 fair till night then Some Rain 26 Cloudy & Some Showrs

27 <u>fair here the whole day</u> but at Barra only 5 Mills from this heavey Rain & Thunder. there has hardly been one day Since the 16 but there has been Voilent Storms of Thunder, & watter Spouts & whirlwinds – in Some places to the North & South of this – & the Same in England & has don a good deal of harm Bridges Carried off & Gulfs Made in the Roads & ground

Jully 1789

28th Peas & Strawberries at Table no Rain but thick fogg at Night 29 Rain – Plenty of Peas & Strawberries now 30 & 31 pritty fair _____

The 1th August got all oor Hay in Tramp Colls in the Yard 2^d Showrs of Rain 3^d & 4^d dry & more wind then for a Long time Collyflowr at Table – this day a Swarm of Bees – the fourth we have got from 4 Stools

5 a great deal of Rain 6 a fair day 7th Some Showrs 8 dry & windy – from this to the 15 fine warm dry weather – That day got the <u>Hay</u> put in Sow

16 17 & 18 the hotest weather we have had this Season – To the 28 very fine weather tho frost Several Nights & after – Showrs of Rain – the Hervest Comeing on in Several Places – Some <u>Bear</u> Cut doun – the 28 a good deal of Rain

from this to the 3^d of Septr Constant Rain & wind – the Rivers & Burns over there Banks & don a good deal of harm to the haugh Corn – 8 Still Rain Every day – a great deal of Bear ready to Cut doun 9 dry – 10 Cut doun oor <u>Bear</u> that night a Sever Frost –

from this to the 14 pritty dry with Some Nights a little Frost Every body Cutting doun Bear 15 a dry day 16 got in oor Bear - a good deal Bear got in – frost Every Night –

17 & 18 dry with frost at night - 19 Rain & wind the whole day 20 More Rain. The River Don over all the Haughs & a good deal of Bear Carried off –

from this to the 24 dry – That day Rain – The Corn Still Green 25 & 26 dry 27 a great deal of Rain 28 more Rain 29 & 30 dry & Vastly Cold

1th Octr A Storm of Rain & wind the whole day – from this to the 12th not twenty four Hours free of Rain, & many days Rain the whole day – The Stouks wate to the Hart – & that on the Ground all Beat doun – & Some of it Springing up again – very little Oats got in – the wind Constantly in the East – that day dry & frost all night –

Tusday the 13th Cut doun Some <u>Corn</u> – 14 the morning dry, but Soon the Rain again & powrd oot <u>all</u> day & all night 15 the Same Constant Rain – 16 & 17 dry got the rest of oor <u>Oats</u> Cut doun –

18 Voilent Rain & wind the whole day much of the Corn Cut – growing Green in the Stouk 19 pritty dry but Rain at Night 20 the Same 21th a Storm of wind – Calm & a great frost at Night 22^d Calm & Suney 23 & 24 drizling kind of fogg with wind

25 dry & windy. dry to the 29 that day the greatest frost we have had – [a great deal of the Crop Cut doun & taken in – Oors all <u>Thachd</u>] – very Cold with Some Showrs of Rain & Slit. 30 a Voilent Storm of wind & Snow & Bitter frost & Cold 31 the Same

Novr 1th the Snow gon & the Air Milder 2 a warm Suney Day till night the Rain begun again, and Continoud all the 3^d a great deal of the Crop Still in the Stouk & to Cut doun South & North & much will be Lost 4 More Rain Came to Abd all round that great fealds to Cut & much in Stouk _____

Novr 1789

29 of Last Month a pritty Sever Shock of an Earthquake was fealt at a little toun near Crife & many Smal ones between that & the End of Agust _____

the 30 & 31 a Voilent Storm Off the Cost of England — more Ships & Lives lost then in any Storm rememberd

---

5th more Rain 6th deluge of Rain & much of the Crop brought doun by the Rivers – betwixt the 6 & 7th a Voilent Storm of wind & Rain the 8 dry 9 Showrs

from this to the 16 Still the Same weather & much of the Crop Rotting Every way & in the South Scotland – & north of England no better –

from the 16 to the 24 not one Day free of Rain 25 More Rain 26 27 28 29th all dry with a little frost at Night which is more fair weather at one time then we have had Since Agust – the Drum going the 27 for Huiks to Cut doun Corn, within Some Mills of Abd – the Crop not all got in yet South nor North 30 dry

The Same Decr 1th 2 Some Rain 3 dry 4 Drizling Rain & wind – from this to the 8 dry with Sometimes very high wind 9 dry 10

Some Rain 11 a fine day the weather all this Month warm Plughing going on Briskly

from the 11 to the 24 often Rain which was Sometimes Snow in the Country often most Voilent Storms of wind & Some nights hard Frost

25 Christmas Day a Voilent Storm of wind & Some Snow – dry windy weather to the End –

1th Jan^ry 1790 Rain – from this to the 10 dry open weather a great deal of wind, & Sometimes a little Frost, & after Showrs of Rain – but nothing to watt the Ground a great deal of the Plughing don – Much Bad Meal this year & the Straw Bad – the Stacks not Hott but Mouldid.

13 Same weather Continowd 15 Still dry open weather 16 frost 17 the Strongest frost we have had

from that to the 23 dry fine weather 24 Some Rain 25 Frost for Some Hours in the morning So Strong as to frize watter in the House over in 2 Hours, but Soon gon 26 Frost but Rain at Night – 27 Cold Blowing day

from this to the 5th of Feb^ry open fine Weather, but We hear of Some frost & Snow up in the high Country

from the 5 to the 12 warm open weather like Spring or Summer from this to the 20 the Same weather – that day windy & at Night a Storm of wind. 21 – 22 – 23 fine days warm as Summer & Every thing advancing as in Spring the Fealds Green all winter & looks all round this as May

24 & 25 the Same – 26 a Voilent Storm of wind fine days like Summer to the End

1 March the Same Cherry Plumb at Kemnay in full Blow of Flowrish 2 Still the Same weather That Day begun Oat Seed at Disblair –

March 1790

12 Still the Same weather – Some days very Blowing, & Some Nights a little Frost, but not to hurt any thing – Oat Seed almost don in Most places

13 & 14 very Blowing Cold & Showrs – 15 & 16 Suny warm days with Some frost at night 21 the Same weather Continowd – The Flowrish on Some aple Trees here almost Blown & pears far advanced –

The Same weather till the 24 we had Soft warm Rain all that day

25 warm fine day frost at Night 26 the Same & the Same to the End of the Month –

April 6 Still the Same weather & not a Showr Since the 25 March Some Nights the Frost very Strong & this day very Cold & heavey Showrs of Hail in the Morning & very Cold –

8 a good deal of Snow in the morning but melted derectly

9 & 10 Showrs of Snow & Cold 11th all whit with Snow & not Melted at 12 Oclock but when the Sune had Shind –

12 13 14 & 15th Every Morning Coverd with Snow but gon Eer Night 16 a little milder & Showrs of Rain 17 the Same 18 thick heavey Sky 19 dry but Cold

Came oot to Disblair the 20 – a fine Suney day The Oat Brire Green but Much hurt with the Weather as is the Grass Larch Green & pritty & the Hathorn – Junkels & Single Narsses Blown, & the Enemones in full Blow but all looking very poorly Pears in full Flowrish & a good deal on the Aple Trees but all looks as droping off –

21 Some Rain begun Bear Seed – from this to the 26 Cold with wind & Showrs of Rain

from this to the 2d May Air a little Milder & Suney but Some frost at Night, but Every thing looking better That Day the 2d Rain Constant all Night & Day we have had no Such Rain Since the 25 March –

3d More Rain & Hail & a great deal of Distant Thunder – 4th Showrs of Rain 5 a great deal of Rain 6 Cold & Some Showrs 7th a fine day –

from this to the 13 warm & Suney but frost Some Nights – The Bear Seed Parks finishd – The Plain Trees Some of the Leaves Expanded Some of the Young Birch now penny Broad-but many of the Old as if winter the Rane & Hors Chesnot begun to Show there Leaves – Strawberries in Flowrish Some Young Gin Trees in Flowrish

14 heavey Sky & not So warm 15 a great deal of Rain & wind & Cold with it 16 dry 17 a great deal of Rain & very Cold

18 fair 19 more Rain & wind & Still very Cold 20th the Ground whit with Frost – Showrs that day 21 a good deal of Thundr & heavey Showrs of Rain & Hail – 22 23 & 24 the Air Milder & no Rain - the Gin Trees in full Flowrish Peas in Flowrish & the Birch may now be Said to be all penny Broad

25 & 26 the Air Colder & frost at night 27 the Ground whit with frost – hot Sune all day – 28 hot Sun frost not So grate fine warm weather to the End

June 1790

1th june 2 & 3d Mild & Some Showrs – 4 5 & 6 Cold as winter

& Showrs of hail & high wind 7 the Same 8 Rain the whole day –
9th high wind & Showrs 10th the Same 11th heavey Showrs of Hail
& Still Excedingly Cold & frost at Night, Every Night 12 fair but as
Cold & frost at Night 13 a little Milder –

The Ash just Come out & the Leaves of it, & other Trees much
hurt by the Frost 14 & 15 the Air warmer & dry 16 & 17 the Same
18 Cold with Rain the most of the day - 19 a Storm of wind

20 dry Cold & windy 21 much the same with Showrs of Rain
22 & 23 Warm fine Days – Could want fire the whol day – a few
Strawberries & Green peas We tasted – 24 Colder with most Voilent
Showrs Hail

25 Rain with a great deal distant Thunder 26 more Rain 27 very
Cold & frost at Night 28 Cold as winter – with heavey Showrs of Hail
– the Groun on the 29 whit with frost at 6 oclock in the morning - 30
Cold with Some drizling Rain

1th Jully Thursday a little warmer 2d Showrs of hail & Rain 3 more
Rain from this to the 8th not a day that Could be Calld warm & often
frost at Night –

Cherries & Strawberries in Plenty where there is Plenty, but that
in very few Places – the Large Fruit will be Scarce Every way. Every
body Cutting doun Hay – Ours Cut the 9th that Crop genraly pritty
Good & the Bear & Oats in good Ground looks well but in Genral
thin & Short –

10 & 11th Rain but only Parshal Showrs always a kind of frost
at Night

16 the Same weather Still Continowed – the Hay much the worse &
lik to Rot 17 Still Cold with Showrs 18 Warm & Mild 19 Cold again
& Sever frost at Night the Ground whit with frost the 20, at 5 oclock
Morning,

21th Showrs at Night a Storm of wind which Continowd Still – 22d
& 23d till Night – from this to the 30th dry weather & Some Nights
a touch of frost

That day a great Storm of Thunder & Hail it begun at half an
Hour after 10 oclock & Continowd without the lest intermition till a
quartr after 3 afternoon the Hail Coverd the Ground for Some Mills
& lay as Whit as a Storm of Snow in Winter, till Night – it was not
gon Next day – The 31 – A very Cold day

1th August Still So Cold as to have fire 2 3 & 4 Still Cold &
windy 5 a little Milder & more Sune 6 Cold & frost at Night 7 &
8 very Cold with Showrs – & frost at Night – the next morning the
ground whit –

from This to the 12 havey Dark Sky, & Showrs of Rain – from

this to the 22 much the Same weather – few days Suney or free of Showrs –

23 & 24 a Storm of wind & much afraid of the Crop being hurt by Loosning the Roots _____

They writ from Kemnay the Bear Crop is quit destroyd by the Hail & frost 30 & 31 of last Month That they are Cutting it doun with the Syth & giveing it to the Beasts not being worth putting in Stack _____

August 1790

from the 24 to the End a good deal of Sune & mild Showrs – Bear Cutting doun by this –

Septr 1 & 2 the same weather – 3d a Storm of wind & Rain all Day – 4 & 5 Still more Rain – Bear mostly for Cutting all Round this but nothing don for the Rain – a great deal Bear & Early Oats Cut about Abd & new Oat Meal in the Market at 10 pence the Peck –

6 Still more Rain 7 the Same 8 a fine Day Warm & Mild – Cut doun oor Bear that was Rip 9th a Deluge of Rain 10 & 11 Showrs of Rain 12 a dry day 13 put the Bear Cut in Stack - 14 pritty dry, 15 & 16 a Storm of Wind has Shaken a good deal Oats –

17 Calmer & pritty fair 18 Rain & drizle the whole Day – 19 heavey Rain all Day & night – the Crop all Laid – the Trees all Yellowd as in the End of Octr Except the Ash 20 Still Rain & wind 21 more fair 22 Cut doun more Bear dry all day

23 Some Rain in the morning but dry the rest of the Day – Cut the last of oor Bear – 24th a fine day, Cut a little Oats was Rip – Eat new Oat Meal – & Bear Meal from the Miln long agoe –

25 Rain all Day 26 Showrs of Rain 27 the Same 28 Rain the whole day 29 pritty fair Cut Some Oats 30 a fine Day got in the first Cut Bear

Octt 1 2d 3 & 4 dry but a thick fogg & frost at Night – 5 a fine open day – the most of the Bear in – a great deal Cut doun & taken in all round this – 6 all oor Oats Cut doun 7th the Bear all in & Thatchd at Night a great deal of rain & high wind

8th Wind & Some Rain – only Skifs – got in Some Oats – 10th the Same & got in Some More Oats – Every Night frost – this day the 11 the pools hard froze a fine Suney Day – 12 a Voilent Storm of Wind & Rain the whole day

13 wind & dry 14 the Same got in all oor Crop & the Stacks all thatchd

15 & 16 dry windy fine day 17 Rain often Frost at night 18 a fine Suney windy day 19 the Same all the Crop around this got in –

20 Cold & Blowing 21 Rain & wind 22 23 the same 24 thick & hazie 25 frost & thick fogg in the Morning – Calm & Suney the rest of the day – the same weather & little frost or Rain till the 29 that day heavey Showrs of Rain 30 & 31 Showrs of Rain –

Novr 1 Rain the whole day 2 & 3 Showrs of Rain 4 & 5 the Same most of the day   Came to Abd - 6 a dulage of Rain & wind all the day 24 Hours. The River Dee was never So high Since 1768 It brought doun a great deal of Corn that was in Hutts on the Haughs & one Stack of Oats. 40 Sheep of one Mans was Carried out to Sea an Once – & many other things –

from this to the 13th Heavey Sky but no Rain – 14 the Same from this to the 19 frost & Clear Suney days – that day Some Rain & wind & heavey Sky 20 frost 21 Some Rain the 22 the Ground whit with Snow & Sever frost

23^d Loud wind & very Cold 24 25 a great deal of Rain from this to the 30 dry & frost at Nights that day Cold heavey Sky & Showrs of Hail

Decr 1790

1 Decr a good deal of Snow 2 Rain & a Strong frost at Night the Road & Pool hard as Iorn the Morning of the 3^d but Rain at Midday, & Continowed all day & Night with Loud wind

4 windy 5th dry & Sunney The Same weather Continowd Loud winds & Some days frost & then Rain – till the 15th when we had Some Snow & a Storm of Loud wind – 16 hard frost & Skifs of Snow 17 wind & frost Exceding Cold a good deal of Snow in the Hills & to the South –

Plughing far advanced Corn & fother up the Country very Cheap & the best Meal 9 pence in the Market –

from this to the 24 Sever frost & always at Night Loud wind 24 Milder & Continowd till the 28 but very Changebel frost & wind to rain – & then frost & wind all in 24 Hours the Same weather to the End –

[the 23 of this Month the most Voilent Storm in London & all the West & to the North of England Ever Seen in that Country a hurrican of Wind with the Loudest Thunder – with Lightning that iluminat the whol Sky – Many Houses unroofed Some Beat to the Ground – the Largest Trees Shiverd, & thrown to the Ground Many People Killd – & many Ships & Lives lost]

Jan^r 1791

1 Day of the Year Rain 2ᵈ the Same 3 in the Morning hard frost, & the Ground whit 4ᵗʰ Rain & Loud wind 5 6 7 Every day Rain with the highest winds We have heard

from this to the 13 Every day very high wind, with Some frost part of the day – then rain – then Wind & frost again – Cold disagreeable weather, & much Loss at Sea – the Ploughing in the Country much keept Back –

14 the Same 15 a Hurican of Wind 16 17 Rain & Voilent wind again 18 Rain – & wind 19 Cold & windy Snow in the far hills

from this to the 27 the Same weather has the Ground Coverd with Snow which lay till the 28 at Night 29 Rain & high wind again – Showrs of Rain Voilent wind Every day till the 2 Feberey

2 Febʳʸ Some Snow 3ᵈ a great deal of Snow, & hard frost (We have not Seen So much Snow this 18 Months) 4 frost – 5 all the Snow gon –

6 7 8 fine Mild Suney days 9 high wind & Skifs of Rain – 10 a fine Suney day

from this to the 22ᵈ one day high Wind & next day Rain Except one Day we had Snow in place of Rain – often frost at Night – That Day the most Voilent Storm of wind we have yet heard –

23 24 25 26 hard frost, the Strongest we have had all winter – from this to the 7 March Changeable weather Rain, wind & frost by turns 8ᵗʰ a fall of Snow, but all gon here next day 9 Cold & Blowing again The above Frost most Sever in England

10 & 11 fine warm Suney Days 12 Rain 13 & 14 dry windy days Every body begining to Sow 15 the Same 16 Rain the whole day –

from this to the 25 much Such weather as it has been Since the begining of the Month the Sowing going on Every way

from this to the End of the Month dry fine weather Oat Seed at Disblair & round that don 28 March the Same weather –

April 1791

to the 3 April – Oat Seed don Every way –＿＿＿＿＿＿＿＿

Cherrie Plumb at Kemnay in flowrish – from this to the 16 Calm weather Sometimes Rain which has been Snow in the Country & frost often at Night

from this to the 20 mild dry fine days & from that to the 25 foggy with drizling Rain – The Same day got Hyacinths and duble Polyanthis Narsiss – & all the difrent kinds of Spring flowrs in full Blow from Disblair –

the Same weather to the End of the Month

1th May Rain 2 Cold & wind 3 the Same The Rain we have had this 8 Days is all Snow in the Hills – from this to 8 frost & Showrs of Snow Every day that day Rain 9 a fine warm day 10 which Day we came to Disblair – warm with a good deal Rain

all the Trees in high Glory many of the Birch penny Broad Some of the Plain in full Leaf all mostly So – Except the Ash – Pear, & aple Flowrish Blown Cherry, & Plumb on the Wall – but no Standerd Trees flowrishd

11 Rain from this to the 15 Air a little warmer with Some Showrs of Rain 16 high wind & very Cold 17 the Same with Showrs of Hail & distant Thundr & at Night Sever frost 18 Some Showrs of Snow & high wind –

from this to the 25 Exceding Cold with wind & Showrs of Rain, & hail, & frost at Night The Grass & Briar much Yellowd 26 & 27 the Air Milder & a good deal of Rain 28 a fine warm Suney day 29 the Same 30 Excedingly warm looks much like Rain 31 the Same with wind

June 1th warm like Summer Peas in Blosom – Gin Trees Lossing there Flowrish – Standerd Trees in full Blosom Pears on the wall well Sett –

from the 1th to the 6 warm like Summer so as to want fire all the day – 6 a hotter day then has been this two years – 7th Some Rain & Air Colder with Some frost at Night 8 a fine day – 9 Cold as winter with Skifs of Rain & frost at Night

10 Bitter Cold so as no wanting fire the Whole day with Showrs of Rain 11th and 12 heavey Showrs of Snow & Hail through the whole Day but the Snow did not ly 13 Snow & Loud wind – 14 Some Showrs of Hail & Rain with wind – a little Milder at Night & no frost – 15 Calm & the Air a little Milder –

from this to the 20 Loud wind heavey foggy Like Sky with Some times drizling Rain frost at Night & Bitter Cold – the Same weather to the 22 – 23 Some Showrs of Rain & the Air Milder

24 heavey Rain the only Rain that Could be Said to watt the Ground Since the Month begun 25 a fine Mild Day 26 a great deal of Rain – no frost this four Nights 27 a fine Mild day 28 havey in the afternoon 29 a great deal more Rain with wind 30 Rain & wind –

Jully the 1th wind with heavey Showrs of Rain 2 a Mild fair day – 3 a Vast deal of Rain 4 & 5 Cold & Wind

from this to the 11 Showrs of Rain & Cold wind Every day Cabage & Turnep at Table not a Straberrie Ready yet not a day we Could want fire this Day the 11th begun to Cut Hay Crop not So good as Uswall

Jully 1791

from this to the 14 Cold with high wind, & drissling Showrs – that day more Sune, & not So Cold.

15 a very hot day, Could want fire for the whol day – Since the 6 of June never Could want fire the whole day – 16 a fine warm day tasted Strawberries & Some whapes of Green Peas are pritty full – the Bear Shot in many Places

16 17 18 Warm days & thick fogg in the Evenings – the Hay all in Tramp Colls in the Corn Yard

from this to the 22 Much the Same Weather – Straberries & Peas in Plenty – from that to the 27 Cold with wind & Skifs of Rain – but nothing to watt the Ground – the Same to the End of the Month

August 1 warm with havey Clouds – the Same to the 8th but no Rain here – tho there has been havey Showrs of Rain in diffrent places – 11 Still no Rain & hot Suny days 12 a fine Showr of Rain 13 & 14 dry & hot 15 a Smal Showr in the Morning, a fine day 16 a good heavey Rain Calm & warm 17 Rain the whole day

from this to the 22 dry & warm Some Bear Cut doun about Abd

from this to the 25 warm fine days that day Colder & Cloudy & Some Skifs of Rain 26 Rain & Cold a little frost at night

28 pritty dry but Cold 29 30 a good deal of Rain & very Cold 31 fair but Cold & a touch of frost at Night

A good deal of Bear & Peas Cut doun in many Places – No Bees have Swarmd this Summer nor in many other diffrent places

Septr 1th Cold wind & flying Showrs 2 & 3 Some Rain with frost at Night 4 a good deal of Rain from this to the 10 fair & pleasent that day Cold wind & drizling – many Smal Parcels of Bear Cut doun

from this to the 15 thick fogg night & morning & fine hot Sun all day – 16 windy Cut doun what Bear was keept unsold – much Bear Cut doun & a good deal taken in –

17 high wind 18 the Same with Rain from this to the 26 fine dry Seasonable weather, & Every body Busie Cutting doun –

this fine weather Continowd till the 3 Octr when we had Some Showrs & thick fogg at night 4th foggy all day with Some drizling Rain 5 heavey Sky with wind & Some Rain

6 7 dry 8 got oor little Hervest finishd

9 a fine day 10 a great deal of Rain 11 Showrs – from this to the 13 frost in the Morning & hot Sune all day – got in that day most of oor Corn but Rain in the afternoon –

14 & 15 a great deal of Rain 16 & 17 Constant Rain day & night 18 the Same 19 pritty fair 20 a voilent Storm of wind & heavey Rain

– 21 frequent Showrs 22 wind & Showrs of Snow & heavey Sky
23 pritty fair 24 dry all day & night – 25 in the Morning dry,
& got in <u>Winter</u> Rain from 11 oclock – 26 More Rain a great deal
to Cut doun & in Stook – pritty fair to the End of the Month & all
Round this Mostly got in –

Novr 1 a fine day 2 & 3 the Same – <u>Came to Abd</u> 4 & 5 the Same
6 hard Frost & a Showr of Snow 7 hard Frost 8 a Showr of Rain &
a fine Suney day from this to the 17 open weather Some days a deal
of Rain then a fine day & then Rain again 19 Showrs of Snow & very
Cold 20 more Snow & frost 21 Rain – a good deal Snow in the Hills
– from this to the End of the Month little frost but high wind with
Showrs of Rain

Decr 1791

Decr 1th hard frost in the Morning & Rain at night 2 the Same 3
hard Frost with a little Snow, which continowd to ly all day Strong
frost at Night & more Snow 4 Showrs of Snow – to the 8 frost that
day a heavey fall of Snow 9 Sever frost with wind bitter Cold _____
10 the Same – 11th frost & Showrs of Snow – 12 a heavey fall of
Snow which Continowd the whol day at night Thaw & then frost 13
fresh & high wind – 14 Snow 15 frost – the Same to the 18 that day
a kind of thaw & frost at night 19 more Snow – traveling very Bad –
the Same weather Continowd to the 23 Frost & Rain & frost again to
the End of the Month

Jan^r 1792

1 Day Milder & thaw with Some Rain 2 & 3 fresh & a good
deal of the Ice Thawd 4 a thick fogg 5 a Strong frost 6 & 7 fresh
& Some Rain 8 Snow & frost 9 More Snow 10 Showrs of Snow &
Strong frost
from this to the 12 the Storm Still encressing & the frost most
Sever 13 & 14 frost 15 Thaw 16 a thick fogg –
from this to the 22 frost & Skifs of Snow that day Some Rain 23 &
24 fogg & drizling Rain – all to the South & in the Country the frosts
have never Brok nor the Snow at any time Lying 2 Inch deep – & no
work don Since Nov^r – at Banff & Nairn they have deep Snow.
25 Rain 26 Rain till 11 at Night – & befor Morn Every thing hard
Froze – 27 frost & 28 Snow & frost – Rain & Frost again – all within
24 Hours 29 Rain 30 fair & Mild 31 the Same
Feb^r 1th frost & very Cold. from this to the 7 little frost & Some
high wind. from this to the 17 open weather pritty dry & warm 18 &
19 frost & Showrs of Snow 24 Cold & frosty with Snow in the Hills

from London 21 the Ground there Coverd with Snow

25 thick & foggy 26 a deal of Rain 27 & 28 thick heavey damp Air. 29 the Same

March the 1 dry 2 & the 3 Rain which Continowd to the 6 when we had Some Snow – the 7 More Snow on the Ground then we had all winter

8 more Snow & hard frost 9 the Same – 10 the frost not So Strong, the Sune Melting a little 11th Voilent frost not Stronger this winter 12 frost & wind – 13 a heavey fall of Snow 14 Showrs of Snow 15 the Same – 16 Rain & wind 17 a fine dry wind & warm 18 Loud wind – 19 the Same (in Some parts begun to Sow) 20 Rain 21 dry & Cold – 22 windy & fair – begun to Sow Oat Seed at Disblair that day 23d Some Rain –

from this to the End of the Month – high wind, & Rain almost Every day - in the afternoon, or Night.

April 1th Very high wind – & Rain at Night 2d the Same from this to the 6th thick drizling Rain – Oat Seed finished at Disblair.

April 1792

7 a fine dry warm day 8 a high wind & Cold - 9 10 11 & 12th all warm dry fine days like Summer – the Hathorn here Green & Goosberry Bushes. Pear flowrish just Bursting

from this to the 16, dry Suny days but Cold Air – from this to the 20 the Same 21 bitter Cold 22 Some Snow 23 a hurrican of Wind 24 a fine day Came out to Disblair Every thing as far Advanced as when We Came out Last Year which was 10 May

25 a fine day 26 Cold and high wind Every body wishing for Rain – the Same disagreable Cold windy weather to the End –

Tuesday 1 May Snow & wind 2 more Snow, Cold as winter & high wind – 3 More Snow & frost 4 Snow lying by the Dyks this morning Mid day Calm & drizling Rain 5 Some Rain 6 the Ground whit with frost in the morning but warmer & hot Sun all day & frost at night –

7 fair & Calm – 8 Cold & winday Every Night frost 9 the Same with Showrs of Snow - 10 Cold as winter, & Snow all the afternoon 12 Exceding Cold –

from that to the 15 Cold with frost 16 Mild & Rain 17 delightfully warm & Sweet & Every thing much refreshd with the Rain 18 the Same & Showrs of Rain 19 a Storm of Wind 20th fair & windy 21 Loud Thunder Rain & Hail which Lay whit as Snow for Many Hours & frost at Night 22 Cold & Rain –

from this to the 25 Cold with frost at Night – that day Milder – & 26 thick fogg in the Morning then heavey Rain & distant Thundr – 27 Warm with Showrs of Rain – 28 & 29 Cold with Rain & thick heavey Sky the whol day –

The Trees all kinds full of Flowrish – & Setting – the Gin Flowrish Mostly Shaken the Peas in full Blosom & the Straberries, Salled ready – Currans & goosberries, like very Smal Peas, but all fallen off & the Stalks mostly quit Stript all the Trees in full Glory Except the Ash – only Some of the Young ones begun to Show there Leaf – Tis very grievous to See them all So hurt with Weather - 30 & 31 Cold with Showrs

june the 1th & 2 the Same weather 3 warm & Suney 4 the Same Could want fire Most of the Day – 5 & 6 Cold again & windy 7 the Same 8 a dry Suney day 9 Cold with Rain

from this to the 13 Voilent heavey Rain Every day & this last Night Frost 14 & Rain 15 the Same 16 & 17 dry & pritty warm & Suney 18 & 19 Rain the whole day 20 More Rain 21 dry Cold Gloomey day 22 Some Suneshine – Some degree of Frost almost Every Night – 23 Fogg & drizely 24 heavey Rain

Nothing has advanced this Eight days, Peas then begun to be in the Pod, not one bit Larger – Clover quit Blackend with the Frost

25 a dry day & a good deal Suneshin 26 27 the Same, & the Air warmer 28 a deal of Rain – 29 a fine warm day - wanted fir for the first time the whol day 23 Cold with Showrs & frost at night

1th Jully dry & Cold 2 the Same 3d a fine warm day with a heavey fall of Rain

from this to the 10 the Air warmer with Showrs of Rain Every day & Sometimes frost at night much the Same weather to the 16 few days without Some Rain & often frost at Night.

Jully 1792

Peas at Table begun to Cut Hay – at Night a heavey Rain, & up the Country Thunder & a deal of Rain –

from this to the 24 dry & [that day The Hay in the Corn Yard in large Tramp Colls – Turnip & Petatoes & Strawberries at Table]

26 thick heavy Sky & Cold wind – [not one Day this whole Summer that Could be Calld very Hott – & often a touch of frost

throw the whole yet the Crop looks well & most of the Bear Shot]

26 Rain at Night & Continoud all 27 Some frost at Night – 28 foggy & about 12 oclock the heavest Dash of Rain I have Seen & Thunder at a great distance 29 more Rain 30 & 31 dry

Augst 1th 1792

The Hottest day we have had this Summer – from this to the 9 fine warm weather & Some day Excedingly Hott & often foggs at Night 10 Showrs of Rain 11 & 12 Gloomy Sky & Closs hot days –

from this to the 19 Closs hot weather Showrs of Rain & little Sune hardly a Breath of wind – the Bear all begining to Chang its Colour.

the Same weather to the 23 that day Thunder & heavey Rain 24 more Rain & the Air quit Cold 25 Rain the whole day & frost at night 26 & 27 28 pritty dry with frost at Night – the Birch & Plain – the Leaves Broun – & falling off –

Many People Cutting doun Bear – 29 pritty fair but up the Country a great deal Thunder & Lightning 30 Rain 31 Rain & fogg all day

Septr 1th 1792

that day fogg in the Morning but Cleard & the Air warmer

2 & 3d Raind almost the whole Day – frost at Night 5 the Same 6 dry 7 dry Cut doun oor Bear 8 dry & frost at night that day windy 9 Rain 10 a Storm of wind with Voilent Showrs of Rain 11th the Same very Cold 12 More Rain Every night

from 13 & 14 Showrs of Rain & Sever frost at Night Cold as if Storm of Snow on the Ground – 15th in the morning Snow Gloomy Cold day & frost at Night – Tops of Petatos & French Beans all taken off –

16 & 17 dry & Sunny 18 most heavey Rain all night & most of the day – Oats Cut in diffrent places – a great deal of the Crop is Laid flat to the ground –

much the Same weather to the 22d 23 new Bear Meal that day Skifs of Rain & frost at Night 24 pritty dry but at night a great deal of Rain – 25 more Rain & bitter Cold – 26 pritty dry 27 the Same 28 begun to Cut Corn – a great deal Cut doun Every way tho not dry or in good Case that day Eat new Oat Meal

29 Still Skifs of Rain & heavey Sky 30 pritty dry –

1th Octr A great deal of Rain – 2 a good deal of wind Every body Cutting doun Much the Same weather to the 6 wind with Skifs of Rain A great deal Cut & taken in Most of Oors in the Yard – & little to Cut

7 dry 8 Rain from this to the 12 Rain Every day & Closs weather
– So as no work Could be don That day a Tempest of wind & Rain
at Night Calm & frost – 13 fair & Cut doun the <u>last of oor Crop</u> – 14
heavey Air & Showrs Much to Cut doun & take in – in many places
& what is in the Staks heating

Octr 1792

15 & 16 fair got in the Most of oor Corn but much to Cut
doun & take in over all this Country
from this to the 22ᵈ Constant Rain Every day & Closs weather
23ᵈ Rain 24 & 25 fair but heavey Air – <u>That day Came to Abd</u>
–

26 & 27 heavey Closs Air & Some drizling Rain –
from this to the 30 Every day Rain 31ᵗʰ pritty dry
1ᵗʰ Novʳ the Same from this to the 4 little Rain
4 5 6 7 Warmer then Most days we had throw the Summer & a
good wind & hardly any Rain 8 the Same – This weather Continoud
till 13 – the Crop now all got in-almost in Every part of this Country
14 Some Rain 15 frost & Exceding Cold – from this to the 20
Bitter Cold – often Rain & frost at Night & the fare Hills Coverd
with Snow that day Some Heavey Showrs of Snow here 21 heave Air
from this to the 30 not a day without Rain Heavey thick Air
with drizling Rain.
1 Decʳ the Same & Continoud to the 5 that night Loud wind
& frost Thursday Rain frost at night 7 a good deal Snow & frost 8
frost till night when We had a most Voilent Storm of wind & Rain 9
Showrs of Rain with wind – that night the wind Rose to Such a hight
that few People remembers to have heard Any thing like it & tho not
So Voilent the whole day
11 Still high wind with Showrs of Snow & bitter Cold 12 Showrs
of Snow with frost 13 Snowd the whole day – thawd at night 14 Rain
– the Snow all gon
from this to the 19 milder weather Some nights frost Showrs of
Rain & wind throw the day – the Same weather till the 22 when we
had Showrs of Snow & frost 23ᵈ More Snow – Every day Some Snow
with frost at night & a kind Thaw or Melting of the Snow the for part
of the Day till the 29 that we had Rain at night a Voilent Storm of
wind Carried of all the Snow – 30 & 31 frost –

Janʳʸ 1ᵗʰ 1793

Rain & wind from this to the 8 frost & Showrs of Snow –
that day Rain, & the Snow all gon

from the 8 to the 16 Rain almost Every day, & often frost at Night – 17 dry all day & a Most Sever frost at night 18 frost Continowd 19 Some Rain

from this to the 24 fine dry days & Some of Shine quit warm – that day Cold & Showrs of Rain 25 Snow – 26 frost 27 28 Some Showrs of Rain 29 & 30 Cold & Blowing 31 Snow & frost

1th Febr a great deal Rain 2 fair & Sunny 3 Rain & frost at night 4 5 & 6 frost 7 the Same & very Cold

from this to the 11 frost at Night & Showrs of Rain throw the day the 11 Snow – 12 13 14 frost at night & Showrs of Rain in the Day – much the Same weather to the 18 that night a Voilent Storm of wind 19 & 20 wind & Showrs

from this to the 24 dry from this to the 28 wind with frost at Night the 28 all Night a most Voilent Storm of wind & Rain –

March the 1th Bitter Cold with high Wind & Showrs of Rain 2 the same at Night a heavey fall of Snow – 3 frost 4 the same 5th Showrs of Snow

from this to the 14 Every day Showrs of Snow dos not lay here but pretty deep in the Country & Sever frost

March 1793

15 the same 16 Rain all Day 17 fair 18 Rain & wind 19 & 20 Rain 21 a deal of Rain 22 Showrs of Rain & frost at Night 23 heavey Sky & a great frost at Night 24 a fair Suneshine Day & frost at Night – this Continoud till 28 when We had a fall of Snow 29 more Snow 30 Snow 31 March Rain –

Abd April 1793

April 1th Rain from that to the 5 Showrs of Rain Every Day

6 fair the Same dry weather with Some frost at night to the 12 that day Showrs of Rain 13 Showrs of Hail & Snow very Cold & frost at Night 14 the Ground Coverd with Snow – & heavey Showrs of Snow – Very little of the Oat Seed in the Ground

from that to the 19 Sever frost, & Showrs of Hail & Snow Every day. 19 the Same – 20 Snow 21 Rain 22 Milder Air, dry with Some wind – which Continoud till the 25 when we had Some Showrs of Rain 26 Rain – 27 pritty dry the Same to the End –

May the first 1 May Rain the whole day 2 a dry day & pritty Mild Came to Disblair

Every thing very Backward Oat Seed don all Round but nobody begun to Bear – no Green on any forest Tree but the Larch – Some Pear Blosom but very little & the Aples not near in Leaf

3 & 4 Showrs & wind & as Cold as winter – from this to the 9 fine dry warm days Some frost at night a great deal of the Bear Seed don – that day drisling Rain 10 & 11 fine dry days 0or <u>Bear Seed</u> finishd

from this to the 15 dry pleasent weather – Every body mostly don with there Bear Seed – that day Cold & windy with drizling Showrs 16 dry all the Trees in pritty full folige Except the Ash – the Birch penny Broad

from this to the 21 dry Clear Suney Days – but often frost at Night 22 & 23 Still no Rain dry Suneshin Days with Cold wind Flowrish quit Blown on all the Trees on the wall 24 the same 25 a Smal drizling Rain most of that 26 dry with wind – that day <u>Cukember Cut</u> –

27 & 28 dry & high wind the last it Snowd all the afternoon & Sever frost at night – 29 it Snowd the whol of the day – & frost at night – it did not ly but Melted with the Sune 30 Still Cold as winter a loud wind & Some Showrs of Snow 31 fair but Exceding Cold – & in the afternoon a great fall of Snow –

1 June high Wind fornoon & the Rest of the day a fall of Rain 2 Cold as Ever & high wind fore part of the day - afternoon Rain 3 dry & windy, 4 the Same

the same to the 8 when we had Some Distant Thunder & a hevey Showr of Rain – that day <u>Cut 2 Melons</u> – the Air Much Milder for Some days past – & no frost.

Goosberries & Currans like Smal peas – Some pears Sett – 9 Showrs of Rain & wind 10 Cold & Showrs of Rain – from this to 16 the Air Still Cold & high wind. Mostly Some Nights frost – 17 bitter Cold high wind & heave Showrs of Hail - frost at Night.

all the Goosberries & Currans dropt of the Bushes 18 a Voilent high Cold wind the whol Day 19 the Same with Skifs of Rain – all the Gins Damsons &c Shaken of the Trees – never one Day this Year We Could want a fire from Morning to Night –

June 1793

this Voilent wind Cold as winter – & often frost at Night Continowd without the list intermition till the 23ᵈ that day was a litle Calmer 24 Calm & Sunshin which we had non of – for a week – but at night frost

25 Cold & More wind again 26 a fine Mild Suneshin day 27 & 28 much the Same 29 Rain the most of the day Cold & Some wind 30 heavey Showrs with Some Thunder.

1ᵗʰ Jully havey Sky with Some Showrs 2 Much the same Mild Air 3 a fine warm Day – wanted a fire till Nigh for the first time this

Summer 4 & 5 much the Same but 6 Rain the whole day 7 Showrs of Rain but warm

8 heavey Sky but no Rain 9 a fine warm day, but Some frost at Night 10 Cold high wind & Some Showrs 11 a great deal of Thunder very Loud – & Lightning – little Rain here but a great deal to the <u>West</u>

12 thick & foggy 13 Some Showrs 14 the Hottest day we have had this Summer 15 thick & drizling Rain here & Some distant thunder –

Turnip & Smal Carrot at Table Cabage well Harted a fortnight agoe – but not one Strawberrie nor Peas ready

16 Cold & Rain & Some Wind 17 & 18 pritty dry Cut the Hay a Very poor Crop 19 dry 20 a deal of Rain 21 & 22 & 23 dry but little Sun & Cold with fogg at Night –

24 a fine warm day & a Sweet Showr at Night 25 very warm & Suneshin - (Some peas at Table & Some Strawberries ready) – a Showr at Night 26 a good deal of Rain & Thunder & frost at night More Strong then we have had all this month

from this to the 2ᵈ August fine warm Calm Seasonable Weather 3 & 4 thick fogg & Some Rain at Night 5 heavey Sky & thick fogg at night 6 & 7 fine warm day 8 a great deal of Rain 9 a fine warm Sunshine day

10 a great deal of rain and Thunder – 11 Showrs of Rain (from the 27 of last Month the weather may be Calld Hot weather)

12 Showrs of Rain & heave Sky – 13 Rain the whol day & Cold – 14 More Rain & frost at Night 15 More Rain

from this to the 28 not one 24 Hours without Rain – Some days a great deal of Rain – others Showrs – Air rather Cold & often Frost at Night 28 Still Cloudy but fair all day

29 a fine day 30 Rain & frost at Nigh 31 Showrs of Rain & a great frost at night –

Septʳ 1 Showrs of rain 2 & 3 Wind & Rain very Cold & frost at Night 4 a Showr of Snow & Slit frost at Night <u>5 fair & Sunshin</u> in the Morning at 10 oclock it becam Cloudy & the <u>Eclipse</u> in the Sun was quit visible till half past 11 when the Sun Shon pritty Bright – afternoon Rain

6 more Rain 7 fair the whole day 8 the Same – 9 Rain most of the day 10 Showrs 11 Rain the whol day 12 & 13 pritty fair & quit warm - Rain at night.

14 Thick fogg all day – & Rain at night 15 heavey Rain 16 & 17 pritty fair, but Some Showrs & frost at Night

18 dry most of the day – Every Body Cutting doun Bear That

day Eat new Bear Meal 19 a fine fair Morning begun to Cut doun
Oor Bear it Continoud fair till night & got the Bear finishd

Septr 1793

20 Rain 21 More Rain 22 dry all day 23 Showrs of Rain 24
Rain in the Morning very heavey the Rest of the day fair & dry all
Night 25 begun to Cut Oats 26 a fine Day good Hervest weather to
the End –

Octr 1th a fine dry Day Every Body Leading or Cutting doun 2
Some Showrs of Rain – Eat New Oat Meal Some days agoe – 3 Cut
doun all oor Oats that was ready But Some Still very Green – & Much
hearabout in that State –

4 a Brisk wind from this to the 7 dry fine weather – that day got in
all the Oats Cut doun 8 Some Rain 9 & 10 fine days 11 a good deal of
Rain 12 a fine day 13 dry with a good deal of wind 14 a fine day – a
great deal Still to Cut doun –

very little frost all this Month – all the flowrs in as great Blow
as any time Summer few of the Trees in their Autom Colour yet –

15 Still a fine day 16 the Same 17 wind with Showrs of Rain 18 a
warm Mild dry Day 19 a heavy Sky (Cut the Last of oor Corn-Still
a great deal to Cut doun & take in)

20 Rain 21 & 22 dry 23 a fine Day warm as Summer 24 Rain
& wind Morning but Calm in the fornoon & very little Rain Came
to Abd 25 fair 26 a dry windy day 27 the Same 28 at Night a most
Voilent Storm of Wind 29 & 30 Some Rain 31 dry

Novr 1th at Night a most heavey Rain 3 & 4 fine days from this to
the 8 Mild fine days & little Rain – that day Some Rain – & Rain &
wind all Night –

the 9 all the fornoon it powrd oot like a watter Spout – with
a tempest of wind – a Ship Stranded & 3 Men Lost 10 Wind &
Some Rain 11 the Same 12 frost in the Morning & a fine day 13
Most heavey Rain – The Crop Now got in Every way Except Some
very late places —

14 & 15 Showrs the wind Still in the East all this Month 16 a
Storm of Voilent wind & Rain for 24 Hours – a Ship thrown in at
the Cove & Beat to peaces – the Cargo all Lost English goods but the
men Saved –

from this to the 21 Rain Every day – 21 & 22 23 thick fogg &
drizling Rain 24 the Same weather 25 a fine day 26 Rain again 27 &
28 thick havey Sky & Showr of Rain 29 Colder but heavy Sky & no
Sun 30 the Same –

Decr 1th a fine fair Day – from this to the 9 fine warm Some days frost – that day Rain the most of the day 10 & 11 the Same Calm & warm – 12 heavey Rain & high wind 13 heavey Rain the whole day 14 more Rain at Night 15 a little frost Morning & fair fore part - Rain at Night

16 Rain & wind 17 a fine fair day 18 Rain 19 Some Rain & bitter Cold 20 a fine day 21 22 pritty fair 23 have Rain all day 24 25 pritty fair 26 the Same 27 heavey Rain –

from this to the thick heavey damp days

Jan^r 1th 1794

1 Jan^r Strong frost Snow in the Hills 2^d the Same 3 Milder 4 & 5 heavey Sky & mild Air 6 the Same 7 fine Suneshin & warm as Summer – 8 Rain & Cold & high wind – 9 Rain in the morning after a fine day

Jan^r 1794

from this to the 19 open fresh weather hardly any frost all the Grass Green as Summer & a great Blow of flowrs in the Garden this fine open weather Continoud till the 24 when we had that Morning a heavy fall of Snow (the first Snow we have Seen all this winter) Snow throw the Day & Strong frost at Night – Loud wind & Snow

25 Snow & wind the whol day 26 Strong frost (all the windows in every derection Coverd with Snow & not melted all that day) – Loud wind & more Snow & the Same throw the Night 27 the Same Sever frost – the wreath of Snow So high all traveling is Stopt no Post from the South – & the Post going oot obliged to return –

no Post for 4 days

28 no Snow throw last Night – but most intence frost – for all the heat of the Houses not a drop from the Sid of any of them – 29 no Post for 4 days 30 more Snow & Sever frost 31th a Brisk wind with Thaw –

Feb^{ry} 1th a warm Mild day & a great deal of the Snow gon 2 the Same Several Ships Lost the 24 & 25 3 & 4 Calm & drizling Rain 5 & 6 Some wind & Showrs 7 a heavey Rain the whole day 8 a Mild fine Sunne Day – 9 Cold & Blowing frost at Night 10 the Same

11 Snow & hard frost 12 Rain & thick Air

from this to the 24 Some Rain Every day – the Same with Some Nights of Loud wind to the End

March 6 Still the Same weather from this to the 9 thick air & drizling Showrs 10 dry 11 & 12 Loud Cold wind & dry air 13 & 14 dry Suney days a little touch of frost at night 15 a warm fine day 16

Cold & wind with Some Rain (Every Body begining to Sow now)

17 a fine dry day 18 the Same 19 a Storm of Rain & wind 20 a fine day from this to the 26 fine dry days Sowing going on Briskly Every Day – Some people Don with Oat Seed – the Same weather Continowd to the End –

April 1th 2 3 fine days & the Oat Seed finishd in Most Places – 4 a great deal of Rain 5 a Storm of wind Rain & Hail 6 a fair day 7 & 8 a Storm of wind & Rain & Exceding Cold 9th 10 11 & 12 the Same weather –

from that to the 21 fine dry weather – but often frost at Night – the Same weather to the End of this Month –

May the 3 Disblair

Came oot here the 30 of April – a fine dry day Bear Seed finishd, the Larch in high Glory the Birch penny Brod the Elm & other Trees the Leaf fare advanced – Except the Ash – all the Trees on the Wall in full Flowrish the Currans & Goosberries Sett – all the Flowrs in full Blow the Hyacinths in the open Ground in full Blow – Rain much wished for –

This day 3d very like Rain the weather very Cold & frost at night – 4 Some Smal Showrs of Rain but Cold 5 & 6 Cold Wind & frost at Night 7 the Same 8 We had Some Thunder & Showrs of Hail in the afternoon –

9 we had Some more Thunder & a fall of Snow & Showrs of Hail – the Air Still very Cold – 10 last night a great deal of Rain – & Thunder today Cold & windy 11 Cold & windy & at night frost the 12 the ground this morn hard with frost

May Disblair 1794

13 Some Rain 14 Cold & windy – Peas in Blosom 15 a fine Mild day – a Large Cukember & Radish at Table – 16 & 17 Cold as winter Showrs of Hail & Snow & frost last night –

21 Calm, & Cold & Some Skifs of Rain 22 Cold & high wind – the Same Continoud to the 28 that day a good deal of Rain but Still as Cold & frost almost Every night – 29 more Mild & Suney 30 the Same – 31 dry with wind

June 1th a fine warm day The 2 & 3d fine Days & warm from this to the 9 Cold & windy & frost Some nights from this to the 13 the Air Still rather Cold & very little Rain but a good deal wind –

from that dry Suney Days & very warm to 17 Could want fire [Goosberries ready for Bakeing Eat Some Peas out of the Pod in the Garden] the Same weather the 18 a Scap Swarmed

19 Still hot Bright Sune from this to the 24 Still warm Mild weather with Soft Showrs of Rain – [That Day 24 had a Dish of Green peas – Some new Petatos – & a Melon at Table]

from that to the 30 Hot dry weather We had a good deal of Distant Thunder & Some fine Soft Rain which is Much Wanted

Jully 2 Some more Showrs the weather Vastly Hot 3 the Same - 4 & 5 the Same dry Hot weather. Feald Turnip all gon off - The 6 the Air a little Cooler but no Rain - Beans Peas & Strawberries now in Plenty –

from the 6 to the 19 as Hot weather as Most People remembers, & not one drop Rain – the Bear Crop all turning Yellow – & many Grass Parks like Stuble after Harvest – That day a Smal Skif of Rain at Night

20 thick heavey Sky, & fogg at Night, & Rain towards the Morning –

21 Rain all the morning, & from Eleven oclock to five afternoon Loud Thunder & Some heavey Showrs – which tis hoped will Save the Crop 22 fair & the Air Cooler in the morning – but a great deal Rain in the afternoon 23 very Like more Rain Some Showrs –

24 dry 25 Some Rain 26 a great deal of Rain – to the End of the Month dry & Cold Air –

1th Agust a good deal Rain & Cold Air 2 more Rain & Cold 3 Rain the whol day 4 fair but So Cold Could not want fire the whol day – Some Bear Cut doun near this the first of this Month

5 & 6 Showrs & Still as Cold from this to the 10 the weather pritty mild & not much Rain 11 & 12 fine Suney days but a little frost at Night

from the 12 to the 20 fine warm Seasonable weather 25 Some Thunder but little Rain a great deal of Bear Cut Doun round this & most Every way, & the Crop Comming fast forward – 27 The weather much the same – Hervest going briskly – New Oat Meal from my Sisters Farm Yesterday – 28 Oat & Bear Meal going in Plenty to the Market – The Same weather Still Continowd to the End

Septr 1th a good deal Rain 2 Some Rain 3 4 5 & 6 good hearvest weather & now many Stacks of Bear & Oats in the Yards - 7 & 8 Still the same fine days & Some frost at Night – That Day don with Hervest

Septr 1794

9 Septr Smokd a Top Swarm of Bees – Honey wighted 40 pd the Same Seasonable to the 13 a fine day got oor little Crop all into the Yard 14 Some Rain 15 dry 16 a Storm of wind & Rain

the whole day 17 Some Rain 18 Showrs frost at Night & very Cold

19 a dry day 20 Morning heavey Rain 21 first a fine day 22 a deal of Rain 23 till Mid day a Voilent Storm of wind & heavey Rain – the wind Continoud all night & Some of the Corns Shaken 24 a fair morning & Every Body Busie at the hook 25 Showrs & wind frost at night

26 Septr this Day the Hills whit with Snow – bitter Cold 27 Cold as winter but fair, & frost at Night 28 Showrs 29 & 30 warm days as Summer, & fair - no frost

Octr 1th the Same 2 the Same 3 Still fine dry warm weather 4 Rain the whole day & frost at Night – Hervest don Every way – the Crop in most places thin & Short –

5 a fine dry day 6 Rain from this to the 23 open weather wind & Showrs of Rain – with frost mostly – Some days fine & warm like Summer – a great many Pears & Aples this Year but not keeping any Time much the Same open weather to the 28 & 29 30 Cold & windy with bright Suneshin – Cam to Abdn 31 the Same

1 Novr fine Suney Days & frost at Night till the 4 when We had in the afternoon the most Voilent Storm of wind & Rain from the East which Continoud till the 7 when the Air was warmer & a fine Calm Suney Day –

from this to the 22 we have hardly had any frost – but Cold mostly & Some Snow in the fare Hills for the first week – this Last week has been a Continoud Storm of Voilent wind from the East with Rain & Showrs of Hail – 3 Ships has been wreckd on this Cost belonging to this place –

the Same weather to the 26 which was a fine Suney frosty day

27 Voilent wind & Rain – havey Sky 28 wind & Rain to the End –

Decr 1th Loud wind & Rain 2 Still windy but dry 3^d a deal of Rain 4 a fair Calm Day

a great deal of Loss by Sea on this Cost

5 Rain the whole Day 6 Rain all the Morning 7 fair & pritty dry till night 8 Rain the Whol Day – 9 & 10 pritty dry 11 Some Rain 12 a fine Clear Sunny Day much the Same inconstant weather to the 19 this kind of inconstant weather wind & Rain hardly any frost Continoud till the 24 that night We had Snow

25 Christmas Day the Ground Coverd with Snow but 26 Eer Night all gon - 27 pritty fair & Continoud So till 30 that Day Showrs of Snow 31 More Snow & Sever Frost –

Jan^r 1th 1795 more Snow & Strong frost 2 the frost very Sever but the Snow not deep 3 the Same 4 Voilent Storm of wind very Cold but the Snow all gon 5 a warm Mild Air 6 the Same fair & warm 7 Some Showrs of Rain 8 thick damp air –

from this to the 12 Intence Frost – that day the Air Milder & heavey Sky 13 the Same 14 Showrs of Snow & bitter Cold 15 the Same – from this to the 22 Every day Sever frost & Showrs of Snow which is now pritty deep – 23 the frost greater then We have Seen for many years - the Storm deep in the Country –

Jan^r 1795

24 & 25 the Frost most Sever. Several things hard Froze in the Room & Kitche of this House – where we have been 14 years – & never Seed any thing Froze befor.

26 Frost the Same with Snow 27 a great deal of Snow – The Storm is now deep & Frost the Snow very great in England the River Thames froze in many places 28 no Post Come in or gon out this day - the Fly for Edn^r Could get no further then Ston hive

29 the Frost Still the Same 30 & 31 Stron frost & non of the Snow gon

1th of Feb^{ry} Some Snow 2 a great deal of Snow 3 the Same 4 5 6 more Snow Every day – & frost as Strong as Ever – all traveling Stopt – 7 a kind of Thaw which Continowd 8 all day – but made little impression on the Snow 9 the same –

10 Rain & wind from the North - & a great deal of the Snow gon all the Houses Cleaar of Snow which Continoud till Night

next Morning the 11th as whit with Snow as Ever & the Snow falling heavily

---

No Coals to be got. All the Ships gon for Coals froze in.

& Continoud till Night 12 more Snow 13 Voilent Frost – all traveling worce then Ever Many days no Post & never Comes at Regular times – tho Many parts both South & north the worst parts of the Roads made passable –

14 more Snow with wind & Sever frost 15 Sever frost the post that Set of from Edn^r that day Arived here on the 17 at the Same Hour he Set off There is now due 5 Mails from London –

18 Sever frost which Continowd with a little of the Snow melting with the heat of the Sune till the 21 when we had a new fall of Snow with wind from the South – Some Ships with Coals arived – which is a great relife – the Snow Still Continoud to Melt here – tho Still frost at Night till the 26 when we had a new fall of Snow

– & all as deep as Ever – There has been no kind of Thaw in the Country

27 a great frost & Clearer Sunny day 28 a great deal more Snow

March 1th Sever frost with wind 2 a new fall of Snow 3 frost 4 & 5 Milder with Rain – 6 more Rain but little of the Snow Melting in the Country 7 frost 8 in the morning the ground & Every thing all Coverd with Snow –

9th a great deal of Rain the new Snow gon but the old firm as Ever – 10 a fine Clear Sunne day – 11 more Rain the whole day – 12 in the Morning all Coverd with Snow – 13 more Snow – 14 Strong frost & bitter Cold 15 the Same 16 a new fall of Snow – frost the Hills never Melted, nor traveling with Carriges Safe on the High Roads –

from this to the 20 no Snow Still very Cold but the Snow much Melted all Round this & Some Plewghing going on, but non in Country –

20 21 & 22 the Air Milder – Some Parks Near Abd Sown with Oats – but no Melting in the high Country, or Hills – from this to the 25 fine Mild weather – that night a Sever frost –

March 1795

26 a fine dry Sunny Day Plughing begun at Disblair – & the Sowing begun in many Parts – but the fare Hills Still Coverd with Snow the 30 Still the Same weather to day the wind got into the South & pritty high – 31 Rain

April 1th Rain the whol day 2d the Same 3 Still Rain The Hills much Shakin 4 frost last night, but a fine fair Suney day 5 & 6 the Same 7 heavey Sky but fair 8 & 9 Rain the whole day & Such a Melting in the Hills that the River Don rose 7 feet perpendicular all work in the Country put a Stop to – all the ground near the River overflowd –

10 Still drizling Rain – 11th a fine warm fair day 12 fogg & drizling Rain 13 Rain 14 Rain 15 pritty dry 16 a fine Day 17 dry & windy 18 warm day with Some Showrs 19 the Same 20 fair & fine Sune –

from this to the End of the Month hardly one day without Shours of Hail –

May the 1th a fine Day from this to the 7 fine Dry warm Days that Day Some Rain – the Oat Seed not yet don in many Places & Seed deep Labouring Still – the Ground So watt

8 this Morning Snow & Hail & bitter Cold 9 & 10 Cold & windy with Some Showrs of Rain & Hail 11th the Same 12 13 wind with Some Showrs 14 very Cold with Showrs of Snow, & at night more Snow 15 in the Country the Snow lying foot deep

& the Hill Coverd – at Night Thick Cake of Ice on Watter in
Abd –

16 more Snow & Hail & Exceding Cold – up the Country the
Snow lies deep – 17 Showrs of Rain 18 the Same but Snow in the
Country as the Hills is Still whit

from this to the 23 the Air very warm – Thunder two days
& Showrs Every Day – that day dry but very Cold 24 the Same

25 Exceding Cold & hevey Showrs of Hail & Snow & Loud wind
26 & 27 Exceding Cold & Showrs of Hail 28 Still Cold with Rain 29
the Same – 30 That day came out to Disblair a fine Mild Day –

the Trees all full of Blosom & all the Trees fully Leafd Except the
Old Ash and Every thing looking better then Could be Expected after
Such weather – the Grass & Briar a little Yellowd – 31 Cold again with
Showrs

1th of June the Same 2d in the morning a most heavey Rain – Cold
& wind all day – 3d dry Milder Air – a great deal of the Gin Flowrish
Blown doun – 4 Rain 5 Fogg & drizling Rain, 6 a great deal of Distant
Thunder – & more Rain throw the Whol Day 7 Rain & very Cold 8
the Same 9 & 10 dry but very Cold Air

11 the Same 12 13 & 15 dry Milder Air, but frost at Night

15 a fine Sunney Day but Cold & a tuch of Frost at Night
– the Peas in full Blosom – Spinage of this Year –

16 Thick Foggy day 17 & 18 fair, but Still Cold 19 Showrs of Hail
frost at Night 20 pritty fair 21 Drissling Rain Cold & Every Night a
touch of frost 22 fair & Sever frost at Night

23 heavey Rain 24 & 25 Still more Rain & Cold as Ever 26 & 27
fair 28 fogg & havey Sky – but no Frost. 29 & 30 Showrs & warmer
Air.

Jully 1th Rain 2 heavey Sky – [not a Strawberry Set Yett – Butt
the Bushes full of Flowrish – Every Tree & Shrub this Year full of
Flowrs the Hathorn whit over] –

Jully 1795

3 & 4 the Same & Still Cold 5 Rain – from this to the 10 fine
warm Days – that day Colder & a good deal of wind & heavy Sky
11 the Same 12 the Same with Som Skifs of Rain 13 a pritty dry day
– have had Turnip & new Petatos at Table – a Rip Straberrie to be
Seen for a wonder –

from the 13 to the 20 dry with a good deal of wind 21 the Same
– & Still touches of frost at Night – the Fruit not Sweeling nor the
Strawberries Ripning – 22 a great deal of Rain 23 & 24 the Same –
a great deal of Thunder & Lightning up the Country –

25 more Rain 26 a fine day 27 begun to Cut Hay, but Still more Rain 28 & 29 pritty dry – a Dish of peas at Table 30 & 31th Rain

August 1th 1795

Still more Rain – from this to the 6 warmer weather then any we have had this year – But Every day Some Rain – very Bad for the New Cut Hay – from this to the 11 Every day Showrs of Rain –

Tis two Months now Since the Peas was in full Blosom & not one peas is Come to full Size yet - Aples & Pears never Swelling & the Aples droping off & the Goosberries as Green as Ever

12 the only Day we Could have Calld Hot this Year 13 Cloudy Got oor Hay into the Yard in Tramp Colls – 14 fogg to the door & drizling Rain the whol day – heavey Rain at Noon – 15 the Same fogg with heavey Rain –

16 & 17 the Same 18 a dry day 19 Rain 20 & 21 the Same 22 dry & 23 the Same Some frost at Night 24 Some Rain in the morning but a fine day 25 a fine day got oor Hay put in Sow 26 Some Showrs

Appendix 1

(The following summaries were stitched into the centre of the Diary)

The Crop of this Year 1784 has much surpassed what any body could have had the lest notion of it has almost dubled what was Expected from it over all this Country. the Meal is now at 9/10- & the best Oat Meal at 10/ the Boll - Some Farms Sold at 9/8

Bear Meal at 6^d the peck Oat Meal in the Market at 7½ and 8 pence the very Best Meal Bear & fother Sold on the ground at 10/ & 11/ the outmost – against the Month of Nov^r, the Bear was giving 20 Shilling in Grain & the Midle of December the Meal was giveing 10^d & 10½ in the Market

the Crop 1785 not turning oot So well –

The Crop 1786 being keept doun by the long Drought the Meal Continoud at 10^d & 10½ in August the Bear give 20 & 21 Shillings Str on the Ground –

In Jan^r 1787 the Oats & fother give 25 Sh the Boll – & Bear 26 – in April the Meal at 14 pence the Peck, in June the Same – in August the Meal giving 12 pence & 12½ the peck – Bear Sold on the Ground at 20 Sh the Boll – End Novr the Meal in the Celers a Shilling the peck – in the Market new Meal 10 pence & 10½ the peck

Jan^r 1788 Meal a Shilling the peck in March the Same – April Plenty of Old Stacks of Corn & Bear in Every Yard – The Fother Plenty, which has made the Labouring go on the Better & the Late Season Less Complaind of – Meal Still a Shilling the Peck August 9 Bear & Corn Roupt of the Ground at 17 Sh the Bear at 17/6 the Boll Corn End of August Meal in the Cellers at 10^d the peck – New Bear Meal in the Market 8^d & 7½ – Midle of Septr New Oat Meal give 11½ –

in Jan^r 1789 Bear & fother. The best at 16 Shillings the Boll – Oats the best 15/ Meal 10^d in Cellers this Year 1789 the River Dee & Don over flowd there Banks Eleven times destroyd much of the Crop on the Haughs Septr Meal giveing 10½ in Jan^{ry} 1790 Meal at 10^d but not good – in Feb^{ry} Meal very good giveing but 9 pence the

122

peck. Best Bear & fother giveing but 8 pund Scotch the Boll.

A Letter from London dated the 10th Jully Says the Ground here was whit this morning – The Storm of the 28 Jully the Hail destroyd Every thing in the Garden at Kemnay – it was in Some places near that 3 foot deep – on the 29 the frost was So Strong as Bear the Wight of a man on the pools – the Bear Crop much hurt by the Hail & Some of the Corn Stript. It was not all Melted the 2 August –

The Meal is Come to a Shilling the peck by the aperance of this Crop proving So late 24 Decr the Crop has turnd out well tho much Loss in the particular parts where the Thunder Storm & Hail 28 Jully – Meal giveing 12 Shillings the Boll 9 Ston – Some at 11 Sh – Many Ships lost on the Cost of England by the Storm of wind the 14 15 this month –

March 9 1791 Meal giveing 10d the peck May Meal giveing 11 pence Malt 17d –

Novr 1792 all this year Meal has been much about 10d The Meal in the Cellers are just now no more Some new Meal in the Market that is very good 1 Sh pr peck

1793 End Febry Meal giveing 15 Sh the Boll a Shilling the peck in the Cellers – in April Meal 16 Shillings the Boll ready Money 13 pence in the Cellars per peck & 14 in the Market Petatos giveing 14 pence the peck –

1793 in August the Crop lookd So ill – & So little Old Meal – that it rose to 15 pence the peck – & Continoud at that price till Octr when it Came doun to 1 Sh the peck.

1794 the Crop all got Safe in not very Rich but Meal & Every thing Reasonable –

1795 the hot & dry Summer made the Crop this year very thin & Short – & the Long Storm made the fother in some places give 42 Shillings the Boll & Bear 34 Sh The Meal keeps doun & only giveing in Cellars 1 Sh pr peck

from the News papers – They had in England the 19 of June this year 1795 Such a fall of Snow as nobody Ever remembers from Pool – & Several of the Sheip Counties. Tis Said the Cold has Killd a fourth part of their Sheep – They being new Cut. We had that day Hail & Sever Frost-as markd in this Book.

Flowr is Excedingly Scarce in London that Inormes Place requirs 20-000 Quarters of whit pr Week - Each Quarter wights 250 pound –

August 1795 there is a great demand for Oat Meal from the South & the Gentlemen are Selling there Farm meal at 15 Shillings & 6 pence pr Boll meal here has keipt a Shilling the Peck as yet but are afraid this will Raise 5 Agust the Meal got up to 14 pence the peck a great deal Ship off

Appendix 2

In Review for 1789

Philosophical Observations on the weather – & dryness of the year 1788 in a letter to Sir Joseph Banks from Mr H of Kimbolton – that only One half of the Rain fell there that year – that fell in Each year. the Seven Years preceding it & that most of that Rain fell on the 20 June – no Less Rain then 2.116 Inches perpendicular. That Rain We had at Disblair near Abd 14 June – See it Markd in this Book 1788.

Appendix 3

Hills Seen from this farm above Disblair - beginning the South

1th Clochnaban
2[d] a Hill in Birse – Mount Battock
3[d] Hill of Fair
4th Mount Skene
5 Lochnagar
6 Corainny
7 Morven
8 Carren William
9 Coreen
10 Millston Hill
11 Bannochie
12 Noth
13 Dunnadeer
14 Culsamand
15 Foudland

3 Mills from Pannach Lodg is Dee Castle – & Belatr – Gray Ston
– & Inch Marle
near that
the Kirk of Mick a Mill on the other Sid the Lodge near it is
Breakly – & a Smal House Calld Marly – Birk Hall not fare from
that

Glossary

Abd, Aberdeen
art, airt, point of the compass
artichocks, artichokes
ashet, dish

bear, beer, kind of barley
birk, birch tree
blick, bleak
braird, brire, breer, brier, briar, first
  shoots of grain etc.

cast, dig, cut (peats &c)
chais, chaise, horse drawn carriage
coll, cole, haycock
could not want a fire, could not do
  without a fire
cukember, cucumber

dulce, must or mould
dush, a downpour (of rain)
dwe, dew
dyck, dyke, stone wall

Edn^r Edinburgh
fare of Hills, far off hills
feltifer, fieldfare
flowrish, blossom
fother, fodder

garret, room within the roof of a
  house
gean, wild cherry
gin, gean or wild cherry

haivery, (of showers of rain) trivial
haugh, river-meadow land
huak, hook or sickle

hutte, temporary shelter for cut corn

junkels, jonquils

kitche, kitchen

latice, lettuce
larx, larch
lyliok, lilac

mavis, song thrush
meal, sometimes intended to mean
  mail
muir burn, heath fire

Narsses, narcissus
New Still, New Style. Dates after
  change of calendar on 2nd
  September 1752 were so designated

rane, raon, rowan tree
ruck, stack

sallat, sallet, salad
scap, beehive
shear, cut (e.g. corn)
shot, (of grain) come into the ear
sine, since
skelly, charlock or wild mustard
socked, soaked
sow, large oblong stack of hay
speat, spate, flood
spinag, spinig, spinage, spinach
Stonhive, Stonehaven
strin, jet of water
strup, strop
stucks, stooks, shocks of cut sheaves

threve, threave,   a measure of cut
  grain consisting of two *stooks*
  usually with twelve sheaves each
toun, town,   a farm with its buildings
  and immediately surrounding area
tramp coll,   a haycock compressed by
  tramping

urie,   ewer

wait, wate, watt,   wet
whap,   pea-pod before fully
  developed
the Wilderness,   an area with a small
  loch and open woodland planted by
  George Burnet close to Kemnay
  House
wreath,   drift (of snow)

Yerd Din,   thunder